AS THEIR FRIENDS
SAW THEM

As
THEIR FRIENDS
SAW THEM

Biographical
Conversations by
BONAMY DOBRÉE

Essay Index Reprint Series

Originally published by:

JONATHAN CAPE

BOOKS FOR LIBRARIES PRESS, INC.
FREEPORT, NEW YORK

First Published 1933
Reprinted 1967

LIBRARY OF CONGRESS CATALOG NUMBER:

67-30183

PRINTED IN THE UNITED STATES OF AMERICA

CONTENTS

PREFACE 7

I SIR JOHN DENHAM 13
by Bishop Henry King and Edmund Waller

II LORD ROCHESTER 33
by Sir George Etherege and Mr. FitzJames

III YOUNG VOLTAIRE 65
by William Congreve and Alexander Pope

IV WILLIAM CONGREVE 75
by Jonathan Swift and John Gay

V THE DUCHESS OF MARLBOROUGH 95
by Alexander Pope and William Pulteney

VI THE DUKE OF NEWCASTLE 115
by Lord Chesterfield and General Irwine

VII LORD CHESTERFIELD 137
by Horace Walpole and Dr. Matthew Maty

PREFACE

THERE are many people who dislike the historical dialogue, and to those — for they will not read this book – this preface is not addressed. But to those who do read this book I would like to explain what it is I have tried to do, being only too conscious that I have not done it.

I have wished to use the dialogue, or rather conversation, form, to give not only character sketches, but brief biographies of the people concerned, the character of the talkers being indicated by the quality of the remarks put into their mouths. I thought it would be interesting to see a person from two points of view, close, and therefore prejudiced points of view. The detachment of the biographer can be carried too far, just as distance in time can be too consciously maintained. We are on the whole right to judge our biographical victims by the standards of our own age, but it may be amusing, sometimes enlightening, to judge them by the standards of theirs.

Two main problems have arisen: the first, how far to confine myself to such remarks only as the talkers are known to have made; or whether, indeed, not to use any at all, a method for which there is a good deal to be said: the second, how far to use the idiom of the day. My practice has varied, for these conversations are, after all, in the nature of experiments, in what is, perhaps, a new, but very limited form. I hope they may amuse the reader. I may confess that for myself, with a desire to write plays (which failure has not eradicated), with a great interest in history, and with a love of the dialogue form, I have felt more pleasure in writing these things than in anything else I have attempted.

B.D.

SOME of these Conversations have appeared in *The Criterion*, *The Nineteenth Century and After*, *Life and Letters*, and *The Nation and Athenæum;* I would wish to thank the editors of these journals for permission to reprint them. *Rochester*, since revised, was originally published by the Hogarth Press, to which I am similarly indebted.

SIR JOHN DENHAM

A Conversation between Bishop Henry King[1] and Edmund Waller; at the Palace, Chichester. March, 1669

WALLER. As I am to visit some friends at Portsmouth, my lord Bishop, I have turned a little off my road from London to carry you some news, which though it will grieve you, I supposed you would rather hear from one who also grieves, than learn from the indifferent words of a stranger or gazette. Sir John Denham is dead.

KING. The motive was kindly and generous, Mr. Waller. I would another occasion had brought you, for though I did not much know Sir John, the loss of so active, and in many ways beautiful a spirit, must always have something of personal about it. Surely he was not old? Of what distemper did he die?

WALLER. He was but fifty-four; nevertheless his frame within and without was cracked and bruised, as much by what life had brought him

---

[1] Author of *The Exequy* and other poems.

as by what it had failed to bring. The death of his second wife, an event made fetid by the breath of infamy, proved too heavy a blow for a mind unhinged already.

KING. I had heard of no infamy. Will jealous tongues never stop their wagging, nor a worthy man be left to taste his sadness in solitude?

WALLER. His wife was young and lovely, over-young, over-lovely to dwell in a Court too dear to me not to wish better than it is. The Duke of York . . . but I need not repeat the kind of idle details too offensively familiar to our ears. My Lady Denham would listen to him on no terms save those of publicity, not wishing to be confounded with the nauseous trapes who flaunt their trails equivocally in Whitehall. Denham was keenly wounded, all the more for the disparity of years, too well remembering his own past, when to outwit an old husband seemed no crime: and, unlike men sterner or more shallow, he let the wound be seen.

KING. Poor soul! We have both known, Mr. Waller, what it is fruitlessly to love, you the living, I, too passionately, the dead. Let us give him our sympathy, for that, I like to think, can never come too late. You smile?

WALLER. I little thought ever to love a bishop the more for his heresy.

KING. Such heresy God will pardon, even though Holy Church ought not. But continue.

WALLER. When Lady Denham died, of a rapid fever, evil tongues bandied the word poison. Some said it was from his hand, others from that of Lady Rochester. So loud was the outcry, that the decent quiet of the obsequies was only procured by the scattering of inordinate largesse to the mob. That honour for the dead should have to be bought from Englishmen!

KING. His mind, you say, was unhinged?

WALLER. Before this time; for while the Court was sniggering and giggling over his marital mischance, he bemused himself with sorrow. Going one day latterly to see the quarries at Portland for some free-stone he required for a building, he walked to within a mile or two of the place, then turned about, having forgot the object of his travels. As he came back to London, he passed through Hounslow, when the occupiers of some houses were astounded to see a tall, slightly bent man — you remember his incurvetting shoulders? — stalk slowly into their dwellings and demand rent. The houses had long ago

B

ceased to belong to him. Afterwards he went to the King and — I hesitate to recount this to your lordship . . .

KING. I am not squeamish.

WALLER. . . . and declared himself to be the Holy Ghost!

KING. It is my turn to smile: such things are not recorded in Heaven. The intemperate spirit hidden beneath a sluggish exterior often breaks out strangely. I call to mind his pale complexion, roughened by the small-pox, his fair hair with its moist curl, and his goose-grey eye, which, though it was not large, nor shining, looked into your thoughts with a strange piercingness when he spoke with you. You were, I think, better acquainted with him than I.

WALLER. I was used to meet him in the Parliament, prior to the Grand Remonstrance; and during the exile in Paris I often saw him at the table I was fortunate enough to be able to keep for our loyal friends. I entered much into conversation with him, and found that his demeanour belied his inward wit. He would brood like a mantic owl, as though indifferent to your converse, then would flash out into some sally of wit, or swiftly moulded rhyme, not always, I fear, too

discreet or seemly. When he stood, he towered
above you, and his laughter would jerk out like
some minor manifestation of Jupiter Tonans,
from the clouds. He joined us late, for he had
been able, you will remember, to gain access to
the Queen, having by some means won the
confidence of the infamous gaoler, Peters, and he
remained long in England to carry on the cipher
correspondence with the Royal Family.

KING. If I recollect truly, it was Mr. Cowley's
handwriting being recognized by the rebels
which led to his discovery.

WALLER. Luckily he escaped, with the Duke of
York, whom he disguised as a girl, and who has
rewarded him at last! But I must not think of it.
He did admirable work in obtaining money from
the Scottish merchants in Poland, decimating
them, as he remarked in his poem on the subject.
It is not among his best writings.

KING. It has always surprised me that such
castigated verse as his could result from an ill-
regulated life. His wild gambling at Oxford,
his equally wild repentance and his book against
play; his immediate relapse after his father's
death into gaming away half his estate, seem a
curious distillery for the clear wine of *Cooper's Hill*.

WALLER.   Yet, early in life he translated the
Æneis, for his 'sluggish exterior', as you have
called it, hid not only an 'intemperate spirit',
but a constant flame, which broke out flam-
boyantly, not in his verse, if we except *The
Sophy*, but in his pranks.   You have heard,
perhaps, how one night he tarred over all the
signs in Fleet Street with a sweeper's brush,
causing chaos and pandemonium the next morning, and dismay in the hearts of the chandlers,
who were far less outraged by the murder of
their king than by the blackening of their placards.
I would willingly see their puffy carcases dangling
for signs outside their squalid booths.

KING.   Let us try to reconcile, in our hearts,
our late unhappy troubles with the better temper
of our fellow-countrymen. Both of us, Mr. Waller,
dwelt much among them at the latter end, and
saw their innate goodness by little and little
overcome the fugitive madness. And Sir John:
where did he go after Paris?

WALLER.   He too returned, but could barely
endure the inaction, for when he could not
exercise his faculties he fretted woefully, and I
much feared his spirit would o'erleap restraint.
It was not his nature to suffer idleness, and where

gentle Mr. Cowley could be happy in contemplation, he could only rage in impotence. He was allowed to live unmolested, for he was no soldier, and the rebels were in his debt for Farnham Castle.

KING. He was too young at that time for so hard a command.

WALLER. Our tempers were not then aroused — I could still sit in the Parliament and say my say — but afterwards, when devilish acts and horrid treachery had incensed every loyal heart and heated us to braver deeds, he might have done more worthily. For it is a hard thing to kill one's countrymen, however just the cause. Who would be an executioner?

KING. There were many things, Mr. Waller, which at the time angered me beyond the charity of a Christian; yet they were indeed fiendish things, and were they to occur again, my blood perhaps would boil once more; for often, to be lukewarm on the side of God is to applaud the Devil. But I must now be very near the period of my days, and from where I stand beside the gates of death, the tumults of life have lost much of their colour and their meaning.

Great as was my horror at the dreadful deeds

of the rebels, it has come to me to think that what they did was beyond the dictates of their will. For human passions are like springs of steel, the more you press them back, the further they will leap to overshoot the mark. It is well in times of anger and riot to give way to what men, however foolishly, believe to be the claims of justice, rather than delay until they take by force what at the beginning the wildest of them would not have conceived as allied to fairness.

WALLER. My cousin Hampden would never have countenanced the death of our saintly sovereign, and Pym himself, though he struck at royalty, would not have aimed at that neck. So my cousin Cromwell earned everlasting shame for a deed the foulness of which darkened even his own cogitations. Yet if excess turned us out, excess brought us back.

KING. You perhaps think, Mr. Waller, that years palsy my thoughts, and that the liveliness of my imagination is clouded with the veil of mortality, but I vow I am much less stirred by the deliberate acts of treachery, such as occasioned the murder of Sir George Lisle and Sir John Lucas than by the wanton acts that defiled our temples. I can forgive the acts of men directed against each other, for alas! blood must pay for blood: but the acts of men directed against God fill me with loathing yet. To carouse in holy vessels, to prostitute copes to the uses of antic dances, to defile altars with faeces, turn churches into stables, and chapels to slaughter-houses, these are horrors greater than the shedding of noble, virtuous, and innocent blood. For the dead have their reward in Heaven; but who can compensate God?

WALLER. The grass at Colchester, they say, my lord, will not grow upon the place wetted by the blood of Lucas and Lisle, though the rank herbage sprouts luxuriantly round about. Where nature abhors, should men condone?

KING. Bitterness is no fitting frame of mind for victors, and I was grieved that the dead were not allowed to lie in peace. We should forget the past and tend the present, for we are not beyond reproach. Were the plague and the fire unmerited visitations? But let us speak of Sir John Denham rather than revive old fevers — and let these funeral offerings of ours not be too sad. He was busied of late, I understand, as surveyor, and his buildings, no doubt, were in conformity with his poetic genius, regular, suave, and proportioned with classical grace.

WALLER. My good friend, Mr. John Evelyn, told me he was a better poet than architect, but Mr. Evelyn perhaps too much admires that 'miraculous youth', as he calls him, Dr. Christopher Wren. Denham was little curious in the mathematics, but he loved order and restraint, though his mind, unlike Mr. Inigo Jones's, was something too subdued to what he worked in. Yet, for my part, I do not dislike his Burlington House, though it reveals little of that airy leaven with which he lightened his stanzas.

KING. He did not write much, I think, during the Rebellion, for indeed, our thoughts were on other things.

WALLER. Our martyred King discouraged him, and, thinking no doubt that a nightingale should sing only in the spring, told him that though he did not mislike his muse, such things were well enough for youth alone, and that graver men should eschew them for business.

KING. As you yourself have done, Mr. Waller.

WALLER. I often wonder if that be matter for praise or blame. It is easy to bustle about the ways of the world, hard to contemplate, and contract one's thoughts into the right span of syllables. Denham was an admirable master of rhyme; he would tolerate nothing superfluous, and his smoothness caused many to deny his solid base. Among the vulgar, cloudiness is often mistook for profundity. He excelled in satire, and showed that the pen, if not, alas! mightier than the sword, can be at least as stinging, and can, like a whip, flick without making a wound.

KING. Satire — and you will forgive my saying this, since I also am among its writers — is not the worthiest object of a poet's hand. At best it can spring from virtuous indignation, and though anger can make good verses, it can never make great ones. Anger builds palings about us such as a poet should ignore. Yet I have often thought that some day a man might arise whose satire would be the outcome of a heart ever bleeding, rather than of a hardened one. Greatly to love a thing is to hate its opposite, or the things that threaten its being; and this new satire will be begotten by humility rather than by pride, as is all that of the ancients. For satire too often descends but to petty vituperation, an idle whipping of the cloaca, and I could wish Sir John had not written that *Dialogue* between Killigrew and Pooley,

witty as it is: for though perhaps Juvenalian,
Juvenal was only great when he ceased to be a
satirist. I like him best when his spirit rises:

> Ite igitur, pueri, linguis animisque faventes
> Sertaque delubris et farra inponite cultris
> Ac mollis ornate focos glaebamque virentem . . .

WALLER. Yet, my lord Bishop, one of the
happiest of Denham's poems is from Martial, and
has a concision, a surety of touch, a sweet singing
note, that would not have shamed Catullus had
he writ in English.

KING. Can you repeat it?

WALLER. I can quote a stanza that contains
more meaning than its unruffled surface would
seem to allow. It is the second of the five, and
runs, if I remember rightly:

> 'Tis not cheeks nor lips nor eyes
>   That I prize,
> Quick conceits, or sharp replies;
> If wise thou wilt appear, and knowing,
>   Repartie, repartie
> To what I'm doing.

I do not excuse the occasion of the poem.

KING. That is very well — but subjects that are merely personal must be treated deeply, as I need not tell you, Mr. Waller. And of all the poems of Sir John Denham I would least readily lose the elegy on Mr. Cowley, which, could my old voice do it justice, I would repeat to you for the mere pleasure of doing so.

WALLER. Pray admit me to the pleasure, my lord. It is the mind, and not the voice which utters the poetry, that conveys us the music we would hear. Whisper it; your attentive congregation will not lose a syllable. You have not to fill your cathedral.

KING. I will omit the first part, which smacks too much of history, and the fine rhapsody at the end, which though it be a little forced, fitly closes the poem: nor will I give you the comparison with Virgil, for such things are otiose. But these are the lines I like to dwell on:

Time, which made them their fame outlive,
To Cowley scarce did ripeness give.
Old mother wit, and nature, gave
Shakespeare and Fletcher all they have;
In Spenser, and in Jonson, art
Of slower nature got the start;

But both in him so equal are,
None knows which bears the happiest share;
To him no author was unknown,
Yet what he wrote was all his own;
He melted not the ancient gold,
Nor, with Ben Jonson, did make bold
To plunder all the Roman stores
Of poets and of orators.
Horace his wit, and Virgil's state,
He did not steal, but emulate;
And when he would like them appear,
Their garb, but not their clothes, did wear.

Those lines I am happy to remember, and often
murmur as I walk in my garden, aromatic with
the herbs Mr. Cowley himself sent me, for
he had a rare and beautiful knowledge in
those matters. But the lines *To the Five Members*
I would miss as little as I do the five members
themselves.

WALLER. Indeed he was best on the things
that touched him most closely, for though *Cooper's
Hill* is a fine poem, an ordered landscape, his
longer ones on *Prudence*, *Old Age*, or *The Progress
of Learning*, have none of them so fine a feeling as
the lines *On the Earl of Strafford's Trial and Death*.

There he earned the interest on the capital he had laid out in reforming our numbers, for even in *Cooper's Hill* there are some things unfitting for a poem. I could never quite stomach his praise of Thames for not being like a mother that overlays her child. His soul did not soar, but he was not devoid of daring, and I think sometimes that he sought in his verse for a clarity he could not attain in life. To profligacy — though he was always temperate — he opposed order, and he loved better to handle the things he could command, than to be tossed in passions to which he felt himself victim. Where he could control he swept, where he could not, he suffered in silence. But you yourself, my lord, have done so much to cleanse our language from imperfections, that I speak under guidance.

KING.   You are too modest, Mr. Waller: it is to you that we all owe a debt. Nevertheless, I think that our new way of writing hinders us from saying some of the things my dear friend, Dr. Donne, could write with such glorious perfection of richness. He has always been my master in those of my writings which displeased me least.

WALLER.   Yet who could better this of Den-

ham's on Strafford, so direct, so compact, so full
of matter and thought:

> Such was his force of eloquence, to make
> The hearers more concerned than he that spake.
> Each seemed to act that part he came to see,
> And none was more a looker-on than he;
> So did he move our passion, some were known
> To wish, for the defence, the crime their own.

KING.   Does it, in its turn, better Mr. Marvell's:

> He nothing common did or mean
> Upon that memorable scene,
> But with his keener eye
> The axe's edge did try.

WALLER.   I was not always so true, my lord,
as I should have been in those trying times, but
that man is a rebel at heart, a friend of Mr., late
Secretary, Milton!

KING.   We are speaking of poetry, not of politics: we should never confuse the two.   In the one
we give form and body to our love, in the other
to our hatred.   Yet those lines of Sir John Denham's, so regular, so antithetical, are to me too
much like a game at tennis, where the net is the
caesura, and each stroke is neatly returned.   I

sometimes regret our old, longer way, the carrying of the thoughts over the lines, like waves coming in upon the shore when the second overtakes the first ere the reflux is exhausted. I am sorry you mislike Dr. Donne.

WALLER. The thought of each age has its fitting measure for use as well as delight: I honour the dead, I cannot wear their dress. We must pay for each gain, and not regret the price. What the future may hold for poetry I cannot see, but the tide has set in one direction, and nothing can check it until it has made high water, to leave upon the shore — what?

KING. I shall not see it, whatever it may be. The customs and modes of my youth are outworn, but I love them, though I have followed the fashions, and not for fashion's sake alone. But so long as underneath the garb the body is clean and strong, as I pray God from now onward in this our England it may always be, we need not fear for poetry: for it is of the essence of things. Though in different measure, as I think (but love and memory may blind me), the same blood flows in our poet's veins be they called Donne or Denham, Cowley, or Mr. Edmund Waller.

WALLER. Nothing, my lord Bishop, can give a

poet more pleasure than the sincere praise of another, and a better; for even though he feel a slight shame at the receipt of unmerited reward, there is in such words a warmth and a reality beside which our triumphs in the Parliament and in the field, beneath the coronet or the mitre, seem cold and exiguous, already of that dust to which some day our verses, however good, must unavoidably return. I would that Denham beyond the grave could hear what we have spoken of him, for I would fain be a heretic in your company.

KING. Goodwill towards the dead can never be offensive to God: and when I die, as in the nature of things I soon must, I should be happily comforted to think that your wishes will go with me on my journey.

JOHN WILMOT, EARL OF
ROCHESTER

JOHN WILMOT, EARL OF ROCHESTER

A Conversation between Sir George Etherege and Mr. FitzJames, at a House in the Street of the Envoys at Ratisbon. Summer, 1686.[1]

ETHEREGE. You can little imagine, Mr. Fitz-James, the pleasure your visit gives to an exile in this gloomy land: for bear it with what fortitude we may, to think of places we love, and of friends we would fain embrace across two hundred leagues, is the most miserable hell the ancients could devise. That it is no laughing matter I am well aware from my damnation here in Germany.

FITZJAMES. Your position, Sir George, should afford you the most various chances for diversion.

ETHEREGE. If enjoyment were not killed by the plague of punctilio, and wit could raise its head

[1] Sir George Etherege was English Envoy at Ratisbon in the reign of James II. FitzJames, who was passing through Ratisbon to attend the siege of Buda, was the son of James II and Arabella Churchill, sister of the future Duke of Marlborough. He was afterwards created Duke of Berwick, and became a Marshal of France.

33

above the beer-rummers! But the sole corantos we dance are about the council-table, and the only mask the ladies wear is that of ceremony. When your royal father sent me here, I little thought I had a grain of love for politics in me, but at this time, I vow, I am more vain of writing a good dispatch than upon my little success in trifles to divert the town.

FITZJAMES. You write no more verses, Sir George?

ETHEREGE. I wear flannel, sir! What have I to do with poetry?

FITZJAMES. My Lord Middleton hoped that here you might find leisure to make us laugh again, and bring to happy birth another Flutter, Dorimant, or Emilia.

ETHEREGE. Alas! I am a fop in my heart, and when removed from the air of the Court, the merely natural cannot please me. What are they about in London now, Mr. FitzJames, in Sir Christopher Wren's new theatre in Drury Lane? Does Mr. Shadwell still make sport with all the follies that are now in fashion?

FITZJAMES. In May I saw a tolerable farce of his, *The Squire of Alsatia*. Sir Charles Sidley, they report, is at a version of Terence's *Eunuch*.

ETHEREGE. I am heartily glad. I have heard him throw off more wit at supper than a dozen trumpery scribblers in five of the longest acts, and hope the world will accord that applause to his writings they have never denied his conversation. Is Mr. Betterton as brave upon the boards as ever?

FITZJAMES. Braver! I have heard Mr. Pepys call him the finest actor he ever saw, while Mrs. Barry improves her talent daily, and ever brings richer pleasure to the sparks and Chédreux in the pit. You look pale, Sir Geogre.

ETHEREGE. A mere vapour! That name awakened memories of a time, Mr. FitzJames, when you were still obedient to the fescue, and ran out in your leisure to eat green gooseberries in the arbour. For in every man's life, however much he may have tasted of the fruits of pleasure, and gained or lost by the frailties of the sex, there is one name will make the blood flow to his face or leave it, even when age has bred idle habits, and he hardly dare offer the lightest tribute to Celia.

FITZJAMES. A thousand pardons, Sir George. Had I known . . .

ETHEREGE. Tut! tut! It is you who must par-

don the consumptive flame of an old lover. Fill
your glass, I pray, Mr. FitzJames. It is the best
I have. Were I not afraid of my canting secretary
listening at the door to accuse me afterwards of
false quantities, I would venture to quote louder
than I do now:

> Antehac nefas depromere Caecubum
> Cellis avitis.

FITZJAMES.   Let me name the toast. I give you
Mrs. Barry.

ETHEREGE.   Mrs. Barry! Admirable creature!
It was of her I was thinking when I described
Emilia's pretty pouting lips, with a little moisture
ever hanging on them, that look like the Provence
rose fresh on the bush, ere the morning sun has
quite drawn up the dew. How badly she acted at
first! No power in her words, no nature in her
movements. What a genius Rochester had in
teaching her!

FITZJAMES.   To most such pupils he taught
another art.

ETHEREGE.   The rogue! Who could gainsay
him? So swift and bright a glance, a face so
delicately fair: the grace of his body, like my
Lord Buckingham's, caught every languishing

eye as he moved, and his laugh was wholly irresistible. But there was an evil humour in him, too, a dark pride like that of Mr. Milton's Satan, and I disputed with him when he caused Mr. Dryden to be cudgelled in Rose Alley, for some pointed verses upon himself which he wilfully authored upon him. For he never could contain the motions of his spirit. Whatever burned in him — love or hate, martial glory, or the fire of the muse — burned fiercely, till life itself consumed to ashes in the ardency of that crucible.

FITZJAMES. My sister, the Princess Anne, told me that she saw him once when she was a tiny child wandering by herself about Whitehall, where my father had brought her. As she walked along a passage, a door suddenly burst open, as though forced by the hubbub behind it, and King Charles came out, tucking his arm under the quivering one of a tall, handsome young man, whose face was flushed with excitement, and whose eye yet glowed as he swore to the King he meant him no disrespect. 'Wilmot, Wilmot!' the King said laughing, but serious behind his smile, 'by rights this hand I hold ought to be hacked off; but then hell would be cheated of just so much of the fuel that is due to it.' With that he spun him round, and sent him along the corridor away from her; and coming towards herself, caught her up, and carried her on his shoulder to where my father was laughing with my mother in an ante-room.

ETHEREGE. We all trembled for Wilmot's hand: he could as well and as shrewdly have struck Tom Killigrew out of the King's presence as in it, and the scandal had not yet ceased when I was employed to the Grand Signior at Constantinople.

FITZJAMES. He was of a violent humour then, Sir George?

ETHEREGE. He ever had too scant respect for whatever seemed a check upon his heat. My Lord Dorset told me that once when he and Wilmot and others were returning to Whitehall after some night frolic, he broke the astronomical crystals under the nose of the sentinel who stood there as stonily as the statues at the gates of Bedlam. As they fell to work, Rochester cried out: 'What! Dost thou stand there to debauch time!' — the word he used I spare your younger ears — breaking a jest to vent the anger of impotence. You never saw him?

FITZJAMES. Some years ago, when I was but a boy with my father at Newmarket. He was pale and a little bent, biting his nether lip in the intervals between his boisterous laughs. 'There,' said my father, 'goes the man who *was* the bravest I ever saw. At the sea fight near Bergen he was the only one who would carry a message in the heat of the action, and his cockle-boat tossed among the fountains made by Dutch shot, as a leaf in the basins of the Mulberry Garden. Yet, lately, on the eve of a fight with Lord Mulgrave, he sent him a letter to say he was sick, and would not meet him. I pray nightly,' my father added, 'that courage may not moulder in my breast, as it has in that man's, as must ever happen to him who not only acts wickedly, but aspires to argue with his Maker.'

ETHEREGE. God forbid! A Stuart was never a coward, and enemies are as likely to see your father's back as I am to catch a Gothic Elector's minister dallying with a vizard. But, Mr. Fitz-James, John Wilmot was no coward either, and if he would not fight John Sheffield, it was from some fantasy he would not give the world, for his mind was ever too high to gratify with reasons the callow emptiness of fools and knaves.

FITZJAMES. I trust I have not offended you, Sir George.

ETHEREGE. 'Fore God, no! I was but warm to hear the idle chatter of the town, which you have yet no reason to mistrust, and are too frankly honourable to withhold. There were men, Mr. FitzJames, who would fawn upon Wilmot in his glory, running like spaniels to his hand when he was made Ranger of Woodstock, and afterwards scuttled about like breathing libels, living lampoons, dropping their poisonous offal on sofas and in Court corners, when he withdrew too darkly into himself, and let them see his scorn. They said he skulked away from his friends when the watch was beaten up: but we were together in such an affray near Epsom shortly before his death, and it was not he who turned aside, nor wilted at the sight of blood.

FITZJAMES. I remember a line of his which seems to belittle courage, suggesting that each man would be a coward if he durst; and it has been said that with my Lord Mulgrave he was putting his verse to the test.

ETHEREGE. Like any Royal Society fantastic? Come, sir! But, in truth, in all his actions he seemed ever to be seeking something others could not see, and would have fled from had they seen it. I have heard him when he was plying the bottle with the rest, all at once quote some lines of Homer — as he told me afterwards they were — and seem to concern himself with ancient heroes and gods, with Telemachus and Pallas, rather than with the company about him. He had powerful parts, and I, who have but gathered my philosophy in the wide world, thinking it more full of flowers than the garden of Epicurus, could never reach his highest thoughts. Indeed, his mind brooked questioning as little as his mood. If he professed atheism — which I detest as deeply as your royal father does — it was because he would not be governed, as much as because he was eager to take his thoughts to the uttermost verge: but he dared also return.

FITZJAMES. Dr. Burnet says that had he lived he would have been the delight of all who knew him.

ETHEREGE. He was, of all who did know him. That babbling busybody! You have met him?

FITZJAMES. I saw him at the Hague, when I visited my sister on my way hither. He sidled up to Prince William as though he thought that if my sister were ever to become Queen of England, the patent for a bishopric would tumble out from her husband's pocket into his hand.

ETHEREGE. Nay, Mr. FitzJames, should the Queen unfortunately give his Majesty no son, there are too many English gentlemen who would rise to resist the Dutchmen, and make way on the throne for someone I need not name.

FITZJAMES. Sir George, I beg! Such thoughts as these sent my cousin Monmouth to a last sad hiding-place among the fern, and his head to an unyielding pillow. Fight for my father I would willingly: I would not raise a finger to succeed him. I love my country; I could not wish to mangle it.

ETHEREGE. You are wise, sir, beyond your years: but as for our plat-banded friend, you are not yet cool enough in blood to see the merit of a man of a kidney foreign to your own. I would trudge a score of miles on the dirtiest night to see John Wilmot once again, and not a yard at noonday to see our Burnet, for he cares for poetry as a fanatic does for prelaty, only to despise it. But he looks you in the face, and if you struck him he would strike you back, and in his own way he has wit. He could never choose between two rights, but he knows what is downright foolish.

FITZJAMES. He wept for Russell.

ETHEREGE. He wept for his friend; his judgment did not gloze his faults. You think it odd in me, Mr. FitzJames, to speak thus, for a badger to applaud a basset. But, in truth, my thoughts were full of Rochester, and my mind often returning to inquire why it was for Burnet that he sent in his last sickness, I have come to see the merits of the priest. For Rochester would seek no porridge faith: it was always meat he hankered after, and there was bone in Burnet to give it him. Wilmot would like his religion to be like his wine, plentiful and strong: he would prefer the vials of wrath to the bosom of Abraham, howsoever warm and downy. He might have been a martyr; he could never have been a saint.

FITZJAMES. The poet Flatman, I remember, in a pastoral on his death, prayed us, 'Live not like Strephon, but like Strephon die.'

ETHEREGE. Flat man indeed! for where would be the virtue of dying like Strephon, if you had not lived like him?

It has been hinted by the pious, Mr. Fitz-James, that my Lords Rochester and Dorset, Sir Charles Sidley and myself, lived only for the flesh — and if even now I have not altogether attained a perfect chastity, I must blame the goodness of my constitution — but, indeed, as you will in time regretfully discover, the flesh is but food for children. My religion — which I ponder in my heart, and prefer to keep there rather than in my tongue, unlike some who make about it as much clack as the water passing through the paper mills of old London Bridge — tells me that to enjoy our faculties is no sin. But alas! we soon weary of the enjoyment, and seek the flesh only to escape from ourselves. A single amour becomes as dull as a single plot in a play, and there is more pleasure in seeing a woman break her fan in anger than her vows in joy. For love is but the reflection of our own youth in a pond spangled with lilies, and the image is shattered when we grasp at a bloom, or even by our breath alone as we approach our faces to see the image closer.

If Wilmot's death was premature, his life was always in advance of his years, and in his thirty-three his thoughts held the compass of a larger life. When after leaving Oxford at fourteen he went abroad in the company of a tutor, he was already too much of a man to be ruled. If the tutor encouraged his love of the muses, he also gave him his taste for opposition, for he thwarted

his pranks, and by his severity taught him bold-
ness and cunning. But of cunning he soon tired;
an intrigue to him became as insipid as a dismal
dinner in a country house, where the gayest noise
in the vast rooms within is the shuffling of the
butler's steps, and nothing is heard without but
the melancholy cawing of the rooks. For it came
to seem as though for him where danger was
absent the dishes lacked salt. When he dwelt at
Blackfriars, in the guise of a German Nostra-
damus, he found the aldermen's wives too easy
to be worth his taking: and at eighteen he
ravished Mrs. Malet from her coach as it was
passing Charing Cross, because she resisted his
flame. But she married him two years later.

FITZJAMES. The spicing of that dish must have
seemed a trifle too high, for I remember hearing
that my uncle Charles was most incensed by this,
and sent him to the Tower.

ETHEREGE. Not for the only time, but never
for many days together. Who could be angry
with Wilmot for long? Indeed he feared nothing,
not the Dutch, nor the devil, nor even the King,
for his wicked rhymes scathed even royalty. He
climbed to the top of daring, and I have sometimes thought that in his pagan vows, his argued

45

worship of Bacchus or the sun, he only sought for something against which to pit himself: and I have even wondered whether in his repentance he did not seek for God only that sin might have a savour.

FITZJAMES. Sir George, you frighten me! Look! I cross myself. But indeed I have heard that he once took one of Mr. Quarles's religious poems, and writing the word 'love' wherever the name of God occurred, sent it to his mistress to declare his ardour. What infamy!

ETHEREGE. I grow too grave. Would you have some music? I have by me a thing of Mr. Purcell's which Mr. Betterton sent me out of his pity, and four of my house can hold the parts tolerably true.

FITZJAMES. I have little ear for music; my fingers could never follow my father's on the guitar: and as my journey has tired me, I beg you not take my excuses ill.

ETHEREGE. Pardon me! I fear I have talked too much, and have been wanting in civility to engross more than my share of speech. My long abstinence has made me over-greedy, for I am weary of entertaining myself with solitude and silence. I abstain.

FITZJAMES. By no means, Sir George: pray continue. Nothing could more gratify me than to hear your recollections of your old friends, especially of such a one as my Lord Rochester. Pray favour me.

ETHEREGE. We will have another bottle. How do you like my German Caecuban? But I beg you, even if it be a little harsh, do not allay it with overmuch Danube, which I have already to thank for a distressing bout or two of tertian ague. I will continue with pleasure, though one is indeed old if one can find the best amusement only in the memory, or dull if the present holds no great delight but the past.

Your mother, Mr. FitzJames, would remember the varied tales about Miss Hobart that used to be bandied about the Court. She was tall, vivacious, and her eye, though hard, had fire. The Mother of the Maids, of the Duchess of York's I mean, feared her influence on her niece, whom she had there with her, and whom she put under the protection of Rochester.

FITZJAMES. As though a wolf in wolf's clothing were less harmful than one in a fleece! Was the wench comely?

ETHEREGE. Comely enough, though she was

D   47

barely even in her salad years, and she became the most moving of creatures, with the most swimming figure, and . . . but our business is not with Sarah, let us call her so here. It is with Miss Temple, another of the Duchess's maids of honour.

FITZJAMES. The one who is now Lady Littleton?

ETHEREGE. With an ever-growing brood of children. Then she was fetching, with soft brown hair, a perfect figure, lingering eyes, a skin like creamy satin, and a welcoming smile that showed even teeth as white as lilies of the valley. But she was vain, gullible, at once confiding and suspicious, prudish and artfully coy, complacent and empty-headed: but in love, so long as the eyes sparkle and the cheek receives a thousand sweeter graces, we do not always ask what lies behind.

FITZJAMES. And did Miss Hobart assist Lord Rochester in his pursuit?

ETHEREGE. She hated him, and tried to thwart him in every way. She had other views, no less scandalous, for Miss Temple, and tried to win her away by luring her with her tall-boy of jams and comfits which the innocent revelled in, neglecting the barbadoes, orange-water, and other chafers of the blood the cupboard entertained, cramming her little mouth as full of sweetmeats as Gargantua his belly with pork.

FITZJAMES. Did not the Duchess or my father take any heed?

ETHEREGE. Your father, if I may say so at this distant date, was then too active in attentions to *la belle Jennings*, your uncle Churchill's wife's sister, to bestir himself in domestic policy; especially as his vows were, to say truth, ill-received: for the Jennings would tumble his unopened *billets-doux* out of her sleeve in the very drawing-room, like an apple-tree showering blossoms. And her Highness, with a steadiness that did honour to her virtue, though no credit to her knowledge, was constant in regarding the whispers about Miss Hobart as old-wives' tales and malicious libels. She not only brought her closer to herself, but helped the devil by giving Mistress Temple into her charge, to screen her from Rochester and Sidney, a mighty pretty youth.

One day in the summer of '64 or '65, in any case before I was as free of the Court as I afterwards grew to be, so I can only speak from hearsay, Temple came back from a ride as hot as a new-baked dumpling, and asked leave to shift in Hobart's chamber, where she could, as she cooled, bury her pretty teeth in the candies. Hobart, whose scheme was ripening, gave no refusal, and wishing to talk with her, invited her to come to the bathing-room within, where, she said, they could speak at their ease, without fear of disturbance from fops or farce-fools.

FITZJAMES. Was my lord Rochester in Miss Temple's graces, or did she, rather, harbour a *tendre* for Sidney?

ETHEREGE. Where Rochester bent his mind, a dozen Sidneys might bend their waists in the most courtly bows in vain. The rogue, seeing Temple mounted on her small acquirements, swore he was dazzled by her brain rather than by her beauties, and would bring his verses to her conquering eyes as though they were the judging ones of Apollo. He would say that had Heaven fashioned him of the stuff that falls victim to outward charms, he would have been lost indeed: but that as, by God's grace, it was only by his soul he could be snared, he was happy to be able to indulge with her in the sweetest converse under the sun without the smallest danger. With such hearty, sincere prologues . . .

FITZJAMES. Sincere, Sir George?

ETHEREGE. In faith, I believe he was sincere, in a sense, for without he could make an amour serious, it was none at all to him. Thus his frank air of honesty ruined many a reputation, and this he cared for more than to gain a kindness. After such prologues, I say, asking humbly for approval, swearing that all that might rival Miss Temple's talents was kneeling there before her in apology, he would present her with his last-wrought satire or song. Such notions turned her pretty, vacant head: but as yet she gave him merely commendation, little thinking he sought only for kisses. But let us return to the bathing-room, which you will find, Mr. FitzJames, not lacking in matter for diversion.

For little Sarah had wheedled permission from Hobart's chamber-wench to wash herself there on occasion, and on this very day was so occupied. Or rather, having filled a bath with cold Thames water, was about to proceed to her business, when she heard Hobart and Temple coming in upon her. She could only in the nick of time draw the curtains that shrouded the bath and slip into the water, when the ladies came in and settled down on a couch to the prettiest little *tête-à-tête* in the world. And Hobart had a plaguy long sermon to preach, to which poor Temple, who smelt no rat, lent her ears with as much alacrity as a dean does to the offer of a mitre: and so did little Sarah, who shivered with the cold water up to her neck till she was as blue as the ribbon of the garter.

'Look,' said Hobart, 'at your suitors. Sidney casts moonlike eyes upon you: Rochester is alert to please, and even Littleton's ponderous sighs grow lighter for your glances. But Sidney is penniless, and would never do for you, apart from things about him you are too young for me to tell you. As for Rochester, if he is the man of most wit in all England, he is also the man of least honour. He is dangerous, but only for our sex, for if we fly from his embraces we are caught by his libels. I'll wager from the things he has said to you, you believe him the sincerest man in the world; but when he has conquered the loveliest creature about the Court, he will not know how to treat you otherwise than he does the wretches all the orange-women in the town are under commission to supply him with. Moreover, he is so eaten up with malice, that already he has paid you court only the more easily to lampoon you. You have reason to look astonished; you may well doubt me; but see here!' With that she pulled from her corset a copy of scurrilous papers Wilmot had written upon Miss Price, who had angered him; accusing her of hideous bodily deformities. Poor Temple, who up till now had swallowed it all down as greedily as she did the raspberry jam in the cupboard, believing the verses for her, was almost in tears with shame and mortification, and left as soon as she could. And Sarah, her teeth chattering like the watchman's rattle, also ran off as soon as might be to warm herself in arms that were used to hold her more closely than is required from those of protectors, and Wilmot was soon made free of the whole tale, without a detail being lost or smudged in the telling.

FITZJAMES.   The wolf had already, then, devoured that lamb?

ETHEREGE.   I have not heard that the lamb ever repined at it: she even came to have a taste for such sacrifices, and grew to an arrant jilt. Wilmot wasted a thousand hells and furies, and would willingly have passed his sword through the Hobart. He swore revenge, and commending Sarah, bade her ever and anon bring him what private news she could discover.

Such a change that day came over poor Temple as made the whole Court wonder at her, and think her sickening for the veil. She showed gloomy and morose, and when a compliment was paid her, sharpened her eyes to daggers. She thought every gallant kept in his pocket those libellous verses of Wilmot's, and had in mind that some vile curiosity was hid by her corsage or farthingale. Her fevered fancy made her suppose each adulation concealed a sneer. When Wilmot came in that evening, she flushed scarlet, then went white as her colberteen scarf, tottered towards him, checked, pulled her gloves up to the elbow, opened and closed her fan, and when he came to salute her, twisted round and offered him her back. Wilmot only smiled, and walking about her to make her manner the more remarkable, said: 'Madam, it passes thought how you can shine after so fatiguing a day. To bear a three hours' ride, and then to undergo Miss Hobart without an eyelid fluttering for weariness, is indeed a proof of spirit.' Temple's eyes blazed like exploding grenades, and Hobart's pinching of her arm made them glow so hot that a deluge of reproaches seemed like to follow. But Wilmot, without stopping to thank Hobart for the turn

54

she had done him, withdrew to wait, while Temple vowed to herself never again to speak with so false a villain.

A few days later, Sarah came post to Wilmot with a story of a merry frisk that Temple, against Hobart's counsels, was determined to play at, which was that the two fillies should swap dresses and parade the Mall in vizards. Wilmot sent for Killigrew — whom he had not yet slapped — and asked for his help to revenge himself. So that evening there was a meeting in the Mall, and Wilmot, pretending to mistake Hobart for Temple, drew her off, while Killigrew, walking with the lively innocent, rated her soundly under the name of Hobart. He told her that all was known of their conversation, that Littleton had sworn to repay her, that the Duchess was incensed at her for some confidences she had made public, and that Wilmot, the most *honnête homme* in the world, would never dream of casting eyes at Miss Temple unless he designed sober marriage. What was more to the purpose, he made so plain to Temple what it was that Hobart intended for her . . .

FITZJAMES. And what was it, Sir George?

ETHEREGE. That I would rather leave unsaid;

but a recital of it was enough to fill the poor girl
with dreadful confusion, and she made off to St.
James's in very near a swoon. There she tore off
Hobart's dress as fast as her trembling fingers
would let her, while Hobart, bewildered by
Temple's flight, hurried to her charge's dressing-
room, where she found her in tears, and ob-
stinately mute except for screaming, which
brought Sarah and the Mother of the Maids,
who poured such a cascade of vituperation upon
Hobart as is rarely heard outside Billingsgate.

In two days the story was in every salon and
chocolate-house, and all the gallants tumbled
over one another to tell Miss Temple that she
had no need to fear that the raillery intended to
Miss Price was meant for, or believed of, the most
beautifully formed of all the maids of honour; so
that in her contrition she resolved to do all in
her power to make amends to Wilmot. But alas!
he was unable to profit by her softened humour,
for at that time he once more incurred the dis-
pleasure of our royal master, and was banished
to the deserts of Oxfordshire.

FITZJAMES. A desert indeed to him.

ETHEREGE. Yet since the Mother of the Maids
was dismissed for making or allowing an idle

tumult, Wilmot did not go to Woodstock alone, for she companioned him, as did also, I need hardly add, Miss Sarah.

FITZJAMES. It is an odd matter, Sir George, that Lord Rochester's most exquisite poems — for I have read them — sing praise of constancy, and vaunt the undying singleness of his flame.

ETHEREGE. Few of us, Mr. FitzJames, have the gift to be constant to ourselves; and I, who have often looked into myself as I idly rolled about the town, have failed to find there what I would. Only the present moment is our own; the past has slipped from our grasp, while the future is not yet, and we cannot claim it — the thought is Wilmot's — and though we may wish our vows were eternal, we have no more right to gird at our fortune if we change, than others have to fleer at our faith.

FITZJAMES. Is not that, Sir George, too easy an excuse for disloyalty? Must men always be reeds shaken in the wilderness of their feelings?

ETHEREGE. Unfaithful Rochester may have been, disloyal never. If he betrayed his wife, he would not suffer her to be insulted, and in his care for his mother, deserved the love she gave him.

FITZJAMES. Even the wolf sometimes remembers his dam.

ETHEREGE. But Wilmot was no wolf, though you have three times called him so. Where trust was given him, he gave trust: when he offered loyalty, he was pained at its refusal or betrayal. When the Duchess of ——, but that name I will cloak, without foundation suspected his integrity (and in truth he had given her the best that was in him), such rebellion was raised against her in his heart, that he never forgave. If he was proud, it was with the pride of the magnanimous that can well forget a blow but cannot pass over a slur. It was easy to open his heart: despite closed it for ever, for the deepest wounds produce the hardest cicatrice.

FITZJAMES. He must indeed have been various.

ETHEREGE. Wilmot had every gift, and what was constant in him was a craze for discovery. Often on some frolic, when as a mountebank or as a merchant, or as companion to the King, he seemed borne on the wings of enjoyment, his face would cloud over: and once at a debauch, when all his wit, his spirit, his abundant grace were more intoxicating than the wine, and he seemed himself to be Pan or the young Bacchus, he clasped my arm till the fingers wounded me, and whispered passionately into my ear: 'It isn't that; it isn't there.'

FITZJAMES.   Unhappy soul to be foiled of even the mean profit of pleasure!

ETHEREGE.   Sometimes, indeed, he complained to us that all life was like the fruit growing by the Dead Sea, which seems so fair a melon when taken in the hand, but when carried to the mouth is more bitter than the Jesuit's powder.

FITZJAMES.   There is a fierce intensity in his satire I have found in no other.

ETHEREGE.   Mr. Marvell rightly said he had the true vein of it, and he himself was no mean inditer of iambics: but indeed, Rochester never rose to the height of my friend Mr. Dryden, though he informs me his *MacFlecknoe* does no good. But even in his lighter verse he was stubborn to reach a conclusion, a virtue most of us lack. His thought does not falter, so his stanzas are not weak about the loins as Sir Charles Sidley's are. My Lord Dorset is the best-natured man — many a frolic I have had with him after the draggle-tailed nymphs can vouch for it — and for that very reason had not the worst-natured muse: but when Rochester wrote, a cold fury

directed him; and always too passionately dis-
satisfied, he came even to the strife of love coldly
though furiously. For five years without a stop
he warmed his thoughts with wine, but in truth
there was little difference between Wilmot drunk
and Wilmot sober, for lodged within him was an
icicle no fumes could thaw, a demon no extrava-
gance could beguile. Sweetness in verse he
learned from Cowley, correctness from Boileau,
but his thought he drew from the founts of
Bandusia, and the fire was of his most private
fuel.

But I see, Mr. FitzJames, your head nods, and
I weary you with my old beaux' chatter. It has
been for me so happy a relief from sixpenny
ombre with martial ladies prouder of their
quarterings than of their colour, and who have
never flirted a fan. Allow me to fill your glass!
No? I cannot leave this ruby to my lacqueys to
swill down their throats, as sensible to flavour as a
plumber's conduits. I drink to your royal father,
Mr. FitzJames, and may you earn all the honours
that are so undoubtedly due to your valour and
your merit.

FITZJAMES. I thank you, Sir George. Indeed I
trust that with the army I shall not disgrace neither

my blood, nor those precepts my uncle Churchill has taught me, who, they say, should occasion arise, is like to make a passable good general.

ETHEREGE. I do not doubt it. Is his wife's hair always as wonderfully gold and abundant? I am glad to think it. I admit her temper would cool my ardour, but I am no soldier, and seek for quiet rather than for conquest.

FITZJAMES. With your permission, Sir George, I will retire.

ETHEREGE. I will light you to your chamber, and to-morrow will accompany you in the coach half a day's journey. I wish you a successful issue of your first campaign.

FITZJAMES. My second, your Excellency: and though last year the Duke of Lorraine would barely let me smell black powder, I hope on this occasion to prove the temper of my sword.

ETHEREGE. A veteran at sixteen! A true Stuart! The fate of Buda is in no doubt. But yet I confess I would not see the starched and solemn Germans too successful. I bear a happy memory of the Turks, and, moreover, our gentlemen of the Diet here will prate so excessively in their High Dutch as to bring despondency into the faces of my good friends Monsieur and Madame de Crécy, who in bringing something of Paris here, have helped me not a little to live. The stairs are steep: pray beware of your footsteps. I will hold the candle higher — tallow, filthy tallow! I hate the smell of frying grease, but wax is as rare here as wit.

FITZJAMES. There is one question, Sir George, that I would ask you. What became of little Sarah, the niece of the Mother of the Maids? I would fain see the features of a wench who would lightly endure freezing.

ETHEREGE. You have indeed seen her, Mr. FitzJames. Her name is Mrs. Barry.

YOUNG VOLTAIRE

YOUNG VOLTAIRE

A Conversation between William Congreve and Alexander Pope. Twickenham. September, 1726.

POPE. Ah! Mr. Congreve! To see you is a rare pleasure. You are seldom abroad. I trust the gout has abated a trifle, and gives you a little ease?

CONGREVE. The warm day tempted me, and my Lady Marlborough had the kindness to say I might employ her coach.

POPE. I was offering myself the pleasure of resting in my new arbour. I would have your opinion of it — and of the burgundy my Lord Bolingbroke sent me t'other day. I will call my servant to give you an arm.

CONGREVE. No, no, I pray: my stick is crutch enough. That walk yonder is really admirable: it deceives the eye so greatly that every time I see it I think it twice as long as it really is. It is as though one looked through a perspective glass by the muzzle end.

POPE. It is not in the style of your friend Sir John Vanbrook.

CONGREVE. Nay, Mr. Pope; he would have put it in his pocket.

POPE. Admire my arb ur! It was not completed when you dined here in July with St. John, Swift, and Gay.

CONGREVE. It is very well. I would Swift had not flown back to his Bœotia; he is the most agreeable of talkers.

POPE. Or would be, if only he could hear what others say. But sit you down: we will watch the sails glide past, and listen to the bleating of the sheep upon the farther side of the river; and, to complete our pastoral — Boy! two flasks of the new wine, and some glasses!

CONGREVE. I like these retreats of ease and contemplation, where we can soothe time in pondering, and perhaps forget our care. Yet the vain intrusions of the world disturb us the more when they occur, and I have not to thank you for delivering me over to a young friend of yours not long since.

POPE. Of mine? Have I friends unknown to me? My enemies are unnumbered — I am one of candour's sacrifices — but a friend?

CONGREVE. Monsieur de Voltaire.

POPE. Ah yes, I remember; he pined to adore

you. Would you not consent to play the idol for the afternoon? Ah! the wine. Your health!

CONGREVE. Yours, Mr. Pope! But idols are not disgracefully fat, nor do they suffer the tortures of gout in the stomach. I cannot abide these runners after notoriety. I saw him advance fawning upon me, and knew he had come so as to be able to nurse the thought that he had met yet another bard, however much decayed. He seemed in a huff when I told him he beheld a plain English gentleman, for he did not wish to see me such as God and my infirmities have made me; he wished to see a name, the name of a man who had, an age ago, toyed with a poet's pen.

POPE. I trust he was not uncivil. You like this wine?

CONGREVE. St. John always had good taste — in wine. Not uncivil, but within measurable distance. He said he would not have put himself out to see me had I not writ *The Way of the World*. After he had gone, I remembered some lines of Boileau I might have quoted, were not my brain so sluggish:

Que le vers ne soient pas votre éternel emploi
Cultivez vos amis, soyez homme de foi;

C'est peu d'être agréable et charmant dans un
  livre,
Il faut savoir encore et converser et vivre.

POPE. As though we were born to do nothing
else but write!

CONGREVE. He seemed to think it the only
employment.

POPE. He has indeed an itch for writing, not
altogether for its own sake, but for *la gloire*.
He would attain in life that princedom given to
poets after they are safely dead: yet he sees himself crowned with laurel, ushered down the ages
by Apollo.

CONGREVE. The myrtle makes a sweeter crown.
But has he written much?

POPE. His *Henriade* ought for length to put
Blackmore to the blush: he would out-Homer
Homer, make Sophocles dwindle beside him, and
outvie Aristotle before breakfast. And haunted
by the fear of dying before he has done these
things, he scribbles a little faster every day.

CONGREVE. Is he sickly? I am sorry if I ruffled
an ailing man.

POPE. Have no fear: he cossets himself like a
queasy woman: if you had done the same when . . .

CONGREVE. Fy upon me! my glass is empty.

POPE. A thousand pardons! there; now it is the flask that is so.

CONGREVE. How did you come to know him?

POPE. He is a friend of St. John's, from his wretched Paris days, and must therefore be one of mine. He has fled from France owing to a drubbing some dandy gave him, and which he bloodily resents, so that . . .

CONGREVE. Better men than he have been cudgelled.

POPE. Mr. Dryden?

CONGREVE. Ay, Dryden, the master of us all.

POPE. In truth, I like the man: he has a white-hot spirit in him, a ferreting mind, with impulses to friendship that must endear him to me. His speech is witty.

CONGREVE. I have heard it said he is a frivolous atheist.

POPE. A Deist, Mr. Congreve, a Deist! Come, both you and I have been accused of impiety. Ah! you laugh.

CONGREVE. Indeed, I grow too censorious. If Monsieur de Voltaire would out-Homer Homer, I must not out-Collier our fanatics.

POPE. He has a swollen admiration for our

country, and would make his people followers of Locke, and think as ours do. He will, I believe, use a sharply satiric pen to work his ends.

CONGREVE. Satire is a weapon to use against poor morals and ill manners; argument and exposition alone can turn the tide of thought. Juvenal is one thing, Lucretius another. But to reform mankind is a wearisome and thankless task. I grew tired of showing men no better than monkeys, to look upon which always gave me mortifying reflections. And to what purpose? Is London nearer heaven than Athens was two thousand years ago? I think, indeed, there is a germ in men which, if they nurture it quietly within themselves separates them from the brute creation, but which is lost in faction and in the desire for fame. I am ageing now, Mr. Pope, and the eagerness of young men carries with it something infinitely pitiful that it hurts me to witness. I grow angry with myself for my pain, and resentful at them for making me angry. It was foolish of me to be vexed at your friend.

POPE. All his life some inward devil will thrust him on; he will think it a wish for the betterment of mankind — which scarce deserves it — but which will nevertheless be for his own advancement. I think also his desire will be given him, for he will never come to see the vanity of writing.

CONGREVE.   Yet what are our desires when we have reached them? We crush the blossom as we pluck it, and though Horace tells us to enjoy to-day, to-morrow is far more surely ours.

POPE.   Another glass of burgundy, Mr. Congreve?

CONGREVE.   You are pleased to banter me; I would not rob myself of your smile by a churlish refusal.

POPE.   It was yours provoked mine; but indeed, self-interest is a cruel taskmaster that will not let us be pleased with to-day.

CONGREVE.   I have ever found the best enjoyment in sitting silently with those I love, watching their bodily graces, and listening to those of their minds as they talk. *Cultivez vos amis!* Wit and cheerfulness I have held dear, yours, and Swift's, and Gay's, and next to the sound of voices that I love, I have doted upon music. To-days have been mine indeed, many to-days that I shall not easily forget; but they have passed, and even while they lasted I could always see beyond them a morrow that had the sunshine without the shadow, the shadow of change, departure, and death. I have, perhaps, dwelt too much in this idle future to have given my friends the comfort that I ought; and now I have come to flee the uncertainty I once imagined gave zest to life, to repose upon the certainties of the past, and the works of the ancients, for they must soon be my everlasting to-morrow.

POPE. And the day after? *La gloire*, Mr. Congreve?

CONGREVE. Ah, Mr. Pope, that uncertainty is too great ever to be enjoyed. Who will think of us in two hundred years, or read our names, except, perchance, upon our tombstones? Let Monsieur de Voltaire carve his niche in that Protean temple if he will, but for me — her Grace's coachman waits. I must hobble back, and leave you to your pastoral hardships. Goodbye, and — do not forget — my service to Mrs. Blount.

WILLIAM CONGREVE

WILLIAM CONGREVE

*A Conversation between Jonathan Swift and John Gay,
at the house of the Duke of Queensberry near London. June, 1730.*[1]

SWIFT. She had his portrait built in wax?
With its chair set ready at table?

GAY. And its doctor to swaddle it against the
gout!

SWIFT. What a piece of work is a man! Faith!
Congreve's fancy itself could scarce have whelped
so gross an absurdity, which indeed smacks more
of Jonson's chimerical satire than of his own
sprightlier wit. Beware, Gay, beware! See what
comes to those who bask in the sunshine of high
ladies. But to-day men of letters are only lap-
dogs, or yelpers to be shut away in distant
deaneries. We are taught the lesson of humility;
it is well to learn it early.

GAY. I listen to your Reverence: I take example.

[1] It is not generally known that Swift paid a last flying
visit to England in 1730; it has, indeed, been universally
ignored by his biographers, and is here made public for
the first time.

SWIFT.   Imp! Incubus! I will deliver you into the hand of Pope; you will vanish as the autumn butterfly, and White's shall know you no more. But tell me, what is this tattle about his will?

GAY.   'He gave what little wealth he had. . . .'

SWIFT.   Don't quote me; tell!

GAY.   . . . to my Lady Marlborough, except a trifle, a year's coach-hire, which he left to the sloe-eyed Bracegirdle.

SWIFT.   What of that?   She mothered him all his last years, and a man may surely pay for his dinners on his death-bed?

GAY.   'Tis just for that the nice moralists of the town blame him, and dub him indelicate. But her Grace has purchased herself a handsome necklace, and devised him a monument in the Abbey.

SWIFT.   And a wax-work in her dining-room. What would they have had him do with his money but endow his private Bedlam?

GAY.   They say Anne Bracegirdle would have put it to better uses.

SWIFT.   And so they would have had him more indelicate just by blaring to the world what it wishes to believe true, and what the lady, veraciously or not, studiously declares to be false.

GAY. Ah! how she must have made an anchorite waver when she first played Angelica and Millamant, thirty years ago now, when, alas! I was too young to be there: but I do not repine, for Congreve did not see young Mrs. Cibber as Polly Peachum, so swift, so clear. They say Bracegirdle was ever tender-hearted to the poor: was she always so cruel to Congreve?

SWIFT. Need we ask? Must the respectable harpies of the world always lick their lips over secrets they cannot probe? In apprehension how like a God, in nostril how like a beast! Is there nothing but the aching senses? Are there not other pains to make men cry for ease?

GAY. For my part, I believe her chaste. You remember 'pious Selinda'?

> Would she could make of me a saint
> Or I of her a sinner.

SWIFT. Yet would he so readily have been a sinner?

GAY. Come, very Reverend Doctor, Congreve was no monster of purity, and knew the universal way of cheating time.

SWIFT. Gay, will you always be a child? Have you not learnt that for every man there comes a time when time will not be cheated? I did not say that Congreve had never sinned.

GAY. But that he feared fruition for the emptiness it would reveal?

SWIFT. Indeed, he had read Suckling too much, though he made Millamant quote him only to ignore his warning.

GAY. Yet I remember those words in *Love for Love*: 'Uncertainty and expectation are the joys of life. Security is an insipid thing, and the overtaking and possessing of a wish discovers the folly of the chase. Never let us know one another better: for the pleasure of the masquerade is done, when we come to show our faces.' But much later he still loved Anne Bracegirdle; he lived in the same street with her that he might see her the more often, though God forbid that I should attach any scandal to that, as some have done; but yet . . . perhaps the good time had once been, and, who knows? the heart may yearn for what the mind rejects.

SWIFT. You also have learnt that wisdom? But then, we are all tongue-lolling foxes, and the grapes are eternally out of reach, the grapes, that is, we know to be the sweetest.

GAY. Yet Congreve tasted so many, from the

plaudits which greeted *Incognita*, even though he knew it for but a graceful trifle, to the better deserved ones which rewarded his plays, till Jeremy Collier came to sour them, and obscure the clear heavens with his stinking, sulphurous smoke.

SWIFT. Collier! A born hedge-parson, cluttered up with the silly jargon of the schools, weighed down by the names of the Fathers of the Church, which he wore ridiculously as a savage wears a necklace of oyster shells, believing them to be pearls. The rabble loved him, and thought the thunder he tried to steal from the prophets was authentic; but a pack of curs, if loudly enough hallooed will always leap at a stag to drag him down, if only because he is the nobler beast. Indeed, Collier was nothing but a heap of farmyard filth, crawling with the worms of envy and dull ambition, who soiled the names of virtue and learning by having them in his mouth, while he brawled and blustered like a fishwife who thinks herself better than her worthier neighbour because she can spell out her book.

GAY. Yet his satire stung.

SWIFT. His satire! He bawled like a bull of Bashan. For all the logic he had learnt he could not reason, so none could reason with him. For me, a man who can think at all can do so without logic, which gives only the appearance of wisdom, and deludes a man into believing he has wit because he can stutter a syllogism. As though truth could be caged in a triangle, one, moreover, of which we shall never find the base.

GAY. True. If you prick out the things about which you may reason, and declare you are only to argue one way, you can scarcely fail always to be right. Which is contrary to nature, though since it flatters man, it is agreeable to what he calls truth. Perhaps that was why Congreve reasoned so ill with Collier.

SWIFT. He did not reason ill, but he used a feather to tickle a pachyderm. Thus all his airiest foolery, such as pretending he had not meant Jehu when he said Jehu, was taken for serious argument, and so was thought by the coffee-houses to be nothing but silly evasion. He was too delicate.

GAY. Even in his satire?

SWIFT. What talk is this you make of satire, my gentle, jesting Gay? Congreve had not the daring to be a satirist, who must be like Milton's eagle which has purged and unscaled its long-abused sight, to look unblinking into the whitest heat of hell. He who, as he said, could not look at a monkey without mortifying reflections, could never steadfastly behold mankind for fear of discovering the ape.

GAY. You talk of him as though he had been a child.

SWIFT. Indeed, I think that for me he was always something of a child, even when his belly would not let him see his toes, and his eyes grew blear with cataract. He was, you see, my junior at Kilkenny, in — do not smile to hear me name so long ago — in '80 or '81, and he followed me to Trinity, where he soon o'ertopped me in height as he did in scholarship. But when I conjure him up in my mind it is of those early years that I think, for when the brain begins to weary, it is the pictures earliest imprinted upon it that remain, the later ones that grow cloudy and dim and faded.

GAY. Almighty Jove! And last year saw *A Modest Proposal!*

SWIFT. I remember him so well in Ireland, before the Revolution drove us both from that land given over to the villainies of Rome, and the cowardice of the worst and most cheating of the

Stuarts. How active he was, for mere sport flinging his lithe body over yawning ditches, his handsome face flushed, and his eager eyes shining
with delight, as when he fished out some darling
passage of Juvenal, or happened upon a rare
piece of Horatian wisdom. But I lost him while I
was with Sir William Temple, and when I saw
him again he was already in the grasp of his
premature infirmities, his work behind him, as
though his flame had been too bright to last, and
his oil had burned itself out.

GAY. From the time I knew him he seemed
eternally dwelling in the days that had been, as if
he were always saying:

> 'For though the present I regret,
> I'm grateful for the past.'

But he was ever delicious, ever thoughtful for
others, our unreproachful poet; yet at his warm-
est he seemed distant and elusive, so that even
when he shook hands, it was the rather like a
friend waving from the end of a street at the
moment when he slips around the corner.

SWIFT. He was an *honnête homme*, as you fashion-
able feathers say. It gave me pleasure to be able
to assure him his place in 1711, when Harley

came in and the Kit-Cats went out, for I was glad to make a worthy man happy. He cared too little for business ever to make a great place, thus not enough to lose a trifling one.

GAY. You think he asked little of life?

SWIFT. Too little, as though he were lastingly afraid of failure, like a child that dares not ask its mother for a toy, for fear it should be refused the plaything.

GAY. Plaything? It was just as such, I thought, that he could not regard life, as far from asking too little of it, he always appeared to me to ask too greatly. His plays seem, in all their most wonderful scenes, to breathe a wish for an existence so exquisite, for beings so lovely in their persons, so delicate in their minds, that in despair he gave over creating them as patterns for mankind to imitate.

SWIFT. It is true he always hated fools.

GAY. Not hate, dear Dean; there was too much pity in his periods to let hate live. But he took no delight in his fools, just because, as you say, he did not want mankind to be monkeys: and since he could not imitate man without making him smaller, he preferred to be silent, to beat up listeners for a concert, write a few verses, or an essay upon the Pindaric Ode. These he might pass around among his friends, for their delectation, and to hear his thoughts echo in their hearts.

SWIFT. Stuff! my angel. He ceased to write plays because the pit would not take *The Way of the World* to its heart. They told me that he came enraged upon the boards, and swore he would write no more for blockheads that could not feel his shafts.

GAY. Say, rather, for ears that could not hear his music. Or was it that his real answer to Collier was *The Way of the World*, whose triumph would have justified him in his own eyes, but whose failure sent him sadly away from the tribunal as a man discountenanced and wronged?

SWIFT. I do not know how far the story is true. No sensible man should gird at the judgments of a rabble, especially of the one that pretends to judge, for that is the most unworthy of them all.

GAY. Are some rabbles worthy then?

SWIFT. Those which the belly goads. Nature gives such wretches a right to howl and to hate. If you dislike a comedy or concert you may stay away, but you cannot for always absent yourself from the stew-pot.

GAY. But here the comedy stayed away from the mob. Small blame to Congreve if he preferred the conversation of the polished.

SWIFT. The polished! as though that were praise! my boots are polished! Nothing is worse for a man of wit than to consort with the progeny of the drawing-rooms, who air what they have heard of Aristotle or Rapin, and do men of genius the honour of using them as foot-rules. A beggar had as well judge of banking, as a man who has never written one of a book. A good book is a fiery thing, a petard placed under the feet of the unwary; but the drawing-rooms seek only for sweetmeats, or at most for a devilled bone.

GAY. He could afford to be prodigal of his sweetmeats.

SWIFT. Nay, I feared, and feared rightly, for Congreve, when he sought for friendship among those who should have been his enemies. For I tell you Gay, we who write are like a small band of adventurers in some rude America, where certain chiefs may do us lip-service, it is true, but where all are ready whenever chance offers a favourable turn, to stab us in the back. We seek for truth, and there is nothing men hate more; we reveal the cancer, while they would cover it up; we burrow under foundations they would like to think secure, and our reward is ashy and bitter.

GAY. Do we not give them beauty?

SWIFT. There is an old song I remember my mother used to sing, very long ago now, 'Beauty is but a painted hell,' and men dread beauty because they scent the hell beneath. When they no longer fear it — for men soon grow to love what is familiar — they are jealous of it, and will defend it, as a woman does her man from the approaches of a younger girl. We are society's everlasting tempest, and the more polished a man is, the more he hates to be ruffled. We must not care if our fellows abhor us. Congreve tasted like gall to men, he should not have groaned at their being harsh to him. We cannot have both the Revolution Settlement and King James III; once blessedly dead, we may not wish to be dragged again to life.

GAY. Yet there was no gall in Congreve, so he gave what he did not possess, or rather, men mistook his sorrow. Just because he grew tired of portraying fools so gross that they should arouse compassion rather than mockery, a wistfulness towards men emanates from his work as pe_fume

86

from the pink. Lady Wishfort's railings show him to be more of a poet than do his Pindaric Odes, though there he was more concerned for right building than for his feeling: but I would say too that there was as much poetry in the folly of old Foresight as in the haunting melody of his songs.

SWIFT. *Love for Love* is indeed his best work; there his learning — he showed how much he brought to it in his *False and Imperfect Citations* — leavened the loaf of the human lumpishness he drew. Then his learned sock was on, and, 'faith, in that play he is more like Jonson than in any other, more, that is, his true son than in *The Old Bachelor*, where he was but his slave and mimic. He had read much, I think, in Marston and in Brome . . .

GAY. And in Cowley.

SWIFT. . . . but it was not for that that I, more than any one else, loved his work. I loved it as I loved the man, which I did for his honesty and his good-will, his sturdiness of humour and his tolerance in judgment.

GAY. You would not give him satire; will you give him gentleness?

SWIFT. Gentleness? No, I will not give him satire, but I cannot deny him the wish.

87

GAY. He declared it in the prologue to *Love for Love*, yet, as though Fate were to underline the denial of his wish, that was his best-liked play. Indeed he laughed at no foolishness but that which no man would own to, and the sentiment is as sweet as the rose. Who more generous than Valentine, more steadfast than Angelica? But in *The Way of the World*, as in his life, he seemed afraid of his own tenderness, as though it were something so fragile that it would break if handled; and he set palings about it, as Millamant did to secure her conjugal affections.

SWIFT. No one has written such prose as he did in those passages, so incisive, so clear.

GAY. Clear indeed; even Dryden could not but admire it . . .

SWIFT. Dryden!

GAY. . . . but it is the clarity of a rippling stream that reflects, not imbibes, the sunlight, to prison it in a lucent box.

SWIFT. A pity his plots were always so tedious or forced.

GAY. He should have stolen them, as Shakespeare did; and I remember his avowing an envy for Terence, who had his fables from Menander, and could apply his ingenuity to the choice of his words. But *The Mourning Bride* had dignity.

SWIFT. Ay, the dignity of a cripple that will not walk too fast for fear of showing how ill his limbs unbend. It was fustian stuff, that 'resistless moan', as poor Dick Steele ridiculously called it.

GAY. You detract from his writings?

SWIFT. What are a man's books to the man himself? It was the latter that I loved.

GAY. Who did not? He quarrelled with none.

SWIFT. Except once with Jacob Tonson, that fretting devil of Whiggery, God knows over what trifle: but the split was of short duration. He had that good-nature for liking men some only give to corpses, which can no longer hurt them, nor wrestle with them in the market-place. Yet he regretted his friends too, and wept for Garth and Rowe.

GAY. I thought he did not seem much to mourn the death of Mr. Addison.

SWIFT. He did not love Addison, he did not know Addison; nobody knew Addison. Who should? He hedged himself about with reserves, till he himself could not break through his own fences without powerful support from burgundy and brandy. I had much to forgive him, but forgiveness was worth while. When Harley, St.

John, and I ruled, he would scarce salute me in the street, though he and Steele had once formed a regular triumvirate with me. He was a prey to the party-spirit he decried and strove against. Congreve was never such: he was simplicity itself compared with Addison, whose soul was a labyrinth which he wished to appear as smooth and innocent as a lawn.

GAY. Thus Mr. Pope could dedicate his *Iliad* to Congreve, but could never have done so to Mr. Secretary Addison?

SWIFT. Congreve avoided strife, and Addison, though he may not have wished it, found himself ever in the centre of yapping puppies. Even when Pope snubbed Philips, or Dennis, Addison received some of the mud that was flung; and when in his grave, Steele and Tickell squabbled over him. He was too much a party man.

GAY. They say the Dean of St. Patrick's . . .

SWIFT. I belonged to no party. I merely allied myself with the honester men.

GAY. Does any man ever do otherwise? We give the name of party not to the cage into which the beasts are driven, but to the beasts which tumble over one another in the cage, kicking up the dust until they all become the same sad colour, and not easily to be distinguished.

SWIFT. Except those that roar louder than the others. But I am now past the hot tempers and unwisdom of tampering with men. I would better my fellows, even though they are not worth the expense of a paragraph, but my paths are not those of the great. Macheath sits upon the Treasury chest, and who knows what Polly pilfers among the guineas; but the wretches in prison — and what a prison! — are still robbed of their ha'pence, and half-naked, struggle like famishing animals when a bone is thrown them. For these we work, to these we minister; but some day, I pray God not far hence, I shall join Stel — I shall join Congreve in the Elysian Fields, and act once more our old Kilkenny. Will *you* mourn for me, Gay?

GAY. Don't, I beseech you! Why are you so cruel?

SWIFT. Ay, for a week: Arbuthnot will grieve a day, and Pope with St. John maybe a little longer. What matter? Once I was young, and Congreve was younger: he did well to go before me, as he was wise to give up the struggle for vain rewards when I had scarce begun. Good-bye, Gay. To-morrow I go to Ireland. It was good to speak of Congreve; it would have been better to remain silent. We like to be stroked, but caresses when applied to half-closed wounds end but by opening them again. Nay, let me be: do not clutch my arm. And call no one; for I have lately thought that when we finally depart, it is well that none should see us go.

THE DUCHESS OF MARLBOROUGH

THE DUCHESS OF
MARLBOROUGH

A Conversation between Alexander Pope and William Pulteney, recently created Earl of Bath. In the Grotto. Twickenham, 1742.

PULTENEY. Good-day, Mr. Pope; may a mortal intrude upon the rural retreat of the muses?

POPE. Oh! who? Ah, I see, Mr. Pult — I beg your pardon, my lord of Bath. Does the coronet sit easy on your brow? Ermine, we know, will become your Roman character.

PULTENEY. Tush, tush! Mr. Pope: you talk like one of the Walpole crew, the gog-magogs, as you used to call 'em. I came away on purpose to be free of the hoots and cat-calls of the idle mob. Am I such a hunted sinner as nowhere to find repose?

POPE. That is as may be; at all events you are not answerable for your sins to me. But have you any?

PULTENEY. None that I can remember.

POPE. Sir Galahad will spur on to fresh

victories now the wicked Merlin has been despatched.

PULTENEY. Do you know, Mr. Pope, I am sad that Walpole has gone — if gone he has; for will he not come plodding up the back-stairs to govern the King? As for me, I feel like a huntsman at the end of the chase: now that the quarry is killed, what more have I to do?

POPE. Sad? Then you are unlike a friend of mine whom I saw a day or two since, who rejoiced almost to heaven for it.

PULTENEY. Not that ridiculous, strutting mannikin, Chesterfield?

POPE. Lord Chesterfield, my Lord, is indeed my friend: I do not choose my companions from among the ridiculous. I knew a man, a commoner he was then, who was once a friend of his, and who . . .

PULTENEY. Mercy! Mercy! Mr. Pope. He has every virtue.

POPE. Ah? No, I meant 'old Marlborough' — I use the term to distinguish her from the younger duchess of the same name.

PULTENEY. Duchess Sarah? I thought she was dying?

POPE. Dying! She defies death, the devil, and

the doctors. She was indeed ill lately. She lay in a stupor for three days, until she heard the voice of authority say over her, 'She must be blistered, or she will die.' At that she raised one eyelid and retorted, 'I won't be blistered, and I won't die!' As usual, she was right.

PULTENEY. Ay, she was always right; at least, she was never known to admit that she was wrong. I have just read her — or rather Mr. Hooke's — *Account of her Conduct*, and an entertaining piece of mock-humble defiance it is. But I wonder how the Queen could have borne with her so great a while.

POPE. It was difficult for Her Majesty not to bear with her: so long as she needed her Captain-General she could hardly part with her Mistress of the Robes. It was only when the Duke with his disastrous policy (your policy, my lord) was blown up by Harley and St. John, that the Queen dared strike at her. She had hated the Duchess, her adored Mrs. Freeman, for years.

PULTENEY. Ha! Mrs. Freeman, Mrs. Morley — dear, devoted Morley! Was anything ever so absurd as those pretended old gossips, whom 'nothing would ever divide but death's impartial hand'?

POPE. Friendship, Mr. Pult — my lord, is not a feeling every man is fitted to judge. For me, to whom friendship is the most valuable thing in the world, more valuable than fame, wealth, or — ermine, well, I am touched by the devotion the Queen displayed to'ards her termagant Mrs. Freeman.

PULTENEY. Her devotion to Lady Masham was every whit as, did you say 'touching'?

POPE. Queen Anne was a woman who needed to be devoted to someone. The Prince of Denmark, drunk or sober, was a dull husband, and all their children died. What was she to do? She did not read, cards and the tea-table were all her amusement, and thus feminine converse was her only serious pastime. It was not she who broke off the friendship.

PULTENEY. It was the chamber-intrigues of Lady Masham, or Abigail Hill as she then was, and a serpent of a woman, which undermined Mrs. Freeman.

POPE. Serpent? Undermined? You have been reading Milton, my lord; or have you perhaps been dipping into controversial theology? Lady Masham, as Dr. Swift, who knew her well before ever I met her used to tell me, was a person of great truth and sincerity, without falsehood or disguise, disinterested in her friendship, and full of love and veneration for the Queen.

PULTENEY. Disinterested? How can the friendship of a penniless woman with a monarch be disinterested? What can royalty do but give? And how can there be friendship between a young woman, not without charm, and an old, decayed heap, fat, slothful, gout-ridden, drugged as often as not with brandy, and without conversation? Disinterested! You will admit that Mrs. Masham tried to get a regiment for her brother, and in so doing very nearly brought about the Duke of Marlborough's resignation, and that she did succeed in having her husband made a peer, in that infamous creation your party manœuvred so as to load us with the Treaty of Utrecht.

POPE. My party! I detest party. You cannot insult me more than by calling me a party man. If I knew St. John, I knew you: if I dined with Swift, I also dined with Congreve. Did I not write a prologue for Mr. Addison's *Cato*?

PULTENEY. Pardon me, Mr. Pope; I did not wish to freshen up old fires, the greying ashes of thirty years ago. It is enough that these memories should redden in old Marlborough's brain; and though you shine as bright as ever, the calm of lengthening years is slowly wrapping me round. The Duchess, you think then, was not outwitted?

POPE. She had always been so dominant, her lust to command had always been so well satisfied, that she grew impervious to the emotions of others; she could never tell what they were feeling about herself, and so thought they would not know what she was feeling about them. Although she raised a memorial to the Queen at Blenheim — it has since crumbled into mud — and never speaks of her but with affection, it is clear that for the last six or seven years of her stay at court, let us say from 1704, she hated the Queen like arsenic.

PULTENEY. I have heard that when handing her Majesty any of her things, she would turn her face away as though her mistress smelt of rottenness.

POPE. Lady Masham used to tell the story, that once when the Queen had left her gloves behind, she sent Lady Masham into the next room to find them — and there was the Duchess sitting reading a letter, and wearing the selfsame gloves. When Lady Masham pointed out her mistake, the Duchess wrenched them off in a passion of disgust, and flinging them on the floor cried, 'Ugh! have I touched anything that belongs to that odious woman!' And the Queen heard it all. Can you wonder that she preferred a compliant, respectful lady-in-waiting, and what the Duchess called 'fawning and flattery', to a woman who hated her, and wanted to make her her tool, to govern her?

PULTENEY. Who did govern her, at least for many years of her life. Who was Queen of England from 1702 to 1708, even till 1710? When I first entered Parliament in 1705, when you were warbling your first pastorals, you will remember that the balladers wrote of her as Queen Zarah. I met her once or twice in those days, imperious and still beautiful, though she had lost that great wealth of hair which so enraptured Colley Cibber when he served her after she had helped her mistress to escape at the Revolution of '88.

POPE. She had cut it off in a fit of pique with the Duke, and then left the room. When she came back she could not find the mesh, discovering it years after among the dead Duke's possessions. She sometimes tells the story, and even now has tears in her eyes as she does so.

PULTENEY. Strange power of fascination! Why, when she was a widow of over sixty, she had an offer of marriage.

POPE. Two, my lord, one from the Earl of Coningsby, one from the Duke of Somerset, and she told the latter that were she only thirty, she would not permit even the Emperor of the world to succeed in that breast once occupied by John, Duke of Marlborough. However, she was not harsh, and was obliging enough to find a more suitable bride for him.

PULTENEY. Her heart seems really to have been dedicated to the Duke; but then he was graceful as well as great, a resplendent husband; and, except in his campaigns, and peccadilloes apart, subservient to her will. I imagine her heart's desire was to have everybody subservient — a most remarkable woman.

POPE. Remarkable for that? Say, rather, a true woman. Have you forgotten the Wife of Bath's tale?

PULTENEY. I cannot read Gothic English. Why should I stumble through Chaucer when I can float upon Homer, Virgil, and Ovid? But what of the Wife of Bath?

POPE. Or rather the young man of her tale,

speaking the wisdom he had learnt — from a woman:

> generally, quod he
> Women desyren to have sovereyntee
> As well over hir husband as hir love,
> And for to been in maistrie him above.

I hope you find no difficulty there.

PULTENEY. As you repeat it, no. But how does it account for the Duchess of Marlborough?

POPE. Search the ruling passion. The husband over whom she desired to have sovereignty was himself a ruler; to govern him, she had to govern — England.

PULTENEY. I wonder, I wonder. Did she really govern England?

POPE. You have just said so.

PULTENEY. Oh yes, yes; but one may have second thoughts. I do not dote upon consistency.

POPE. So the world has recently been privileged to observe, my lord.

PULTENEY. Little the world knows about it. Have I accepted office?

POPE. The Right Honourable the Earl of Bath.

PULTENEY. Pooh! What does that imply? Is that reward? Why, that fellow Walpole,

Orford, came up to me in the House of Lords the other day and said, 'Here we are, my lord, the two most insignificant fellows in England!' I almost forgave him all for the sake of that thrust.

POPE. But let me hear why, in the last few minutes, you have changed your mind about Queen Sarah.

PULTENEY. Granted that in the early years of the reign she changed Queen Anne, temporarily, from a Tory to a Whig — though indeed the Tories did that as much as anybody with the insults they showered upon her — granted that she welded the Duke and Godolphin to her purposes by means of her furious determination, was it not that very fury that in the end ruined her party? If she had been less domineering over the Queen, would the Queen have been so eager to dismiss the Duke? Her Majesty rebelled against the slavery: she need not have been aware of it but for her Mistress of the Robes. A clever minister makes his monarch a willing slave. Walpole was acute enough to see that, and it would appear that Carteret has learnt the lesson.

POPE. I often admire the humility of you politicians.

PULTENEY. Well, have I mis-stated the case?

POPE. You forget that though a monarch may seem a slave, he chooses his own slave-driver; at the worst, he chooses among slave-drivers. Also you forget that in the instance we are now discussing, it takes two to make a friendship. It was as friendship that Duchess Sarah's rule began; and she certainly was a good friend at the Revolution, when she spirited the Princess away at the critical moment: they were two young women conquering the world: and she was a better friend still when she fought Dutch William on behalf of the Princess's allowance, and thereby incurred her own disgrace, and banishment from court. And where, among friends, one is much the stronger, the strong one's feeling will often, even inevitably, turn to dominance, to driving the weaker one in the direction which seems to lead to the greatest success. Oh, the Duchess liked to drive; but again, if she seems to have driven the Duke into his war policy, was it not that he wanted to go that way?

PULTENEY. And in the end it was the Queen's obstinacy that won. Old Marlborough does not seem to taste the comedy of the scene she describes, when she pursued the Queen to Kensington, implored an explanation of her coldness in a flood of tears, and was met only by the maddening iteration of the same reply, 'You desired no answer, and you shall have none'. Yet, after all, it was the Harley, St. John, Masham cabal that ruined us, and brought about the degradation of Utrecht.

POPE. Again the humility of politicians! Was it you, or St. John, or anybody, that brought about the events of the reign? — or of any reign? Are you not also tools of men's passions. And is there not something behind men's passions directed by some Higher Will, something working for the Universal Good? There's a divinity which shapes our ends, rough-hew them how we will. You read Shakespeare, my lord?

PULTENEY. Since you have edited him, yes. But if we are going to talk philosophy, St. John . . .

POPE. Some people call it religion.

PULTENEY. Then we had better change the subject. Let me ask, Mr. Pope, if I may without a probing impertinence, what is it that makes you pass so much of your time with Old Marlborough? Is it pity?

POPE. Pity! Do you pity the lioness?

PULTENEY. Perhaps: when age has withered the sinews, time pared the claws.

POPE. The sinews of her spirit will never be weakened while she lives; and her claws are still sharp enough.

PULTENEY. But it is only her family that she can scrabble — and I, for my part, find it a little pitiable. It is spirited, yes, to fight the present Duke in the law-courts, and swear that he should never keep the sword her lord would have borne to Paris, but which his descendant would carry to the pawn-brokers to pledge the jewels in the hilt. It is amusing of her to paint black enamel over the portrait of Lady Anne Bateman, and write beneath, 'She is blacker within': there is wit in having puppets made to represent her cousins the Trevors stealing the furniture, digging up the shrubs of the house she had rented them, and running off with the hen-coops under their arms. But then, she who once ruled the destinies of Europe, to be reduced to the squabbles of a kitchen-maid!

POPE. Fighting is her life-blood; from her birth, she's made her life one warfare upon earth.

PULTENEY. Rhymes, Mr. Pope? Metre? Are you meditating a scathing satire?

POPE. On my friend? God forbid! I but
state a fact. I see no blame in it, though such a
life I, who care but for quiet and the converse of
friends, do not think the one to wish for. She was
always more pugnacious than her lord: she has
ever revelled in battle, and her nostrils widen to
its faintest scent. She quarrelled with Sir John
Vanbrugh, you remember, most genial of men;
she fought with the Duke of St. Albans over her
right to drive through the royal parks; the only
friend she never ranged herself against was
Godolphin — and him she harried into a Whiggery he was not very partial to. She has thought
your party of *patriots*, my lord, feeble reeds,
and complained bitterly to me that when she
pressed you doughty warriors to engage, all she
could get was that you hoped some accident
might bring things to a better pass.

PULTENEY. She should be content now that
the change has come.

POPE. Change? Two patriots kissing hands
at court? The only two of you for whom she has
any regard left are Lord Chesterfield, and Mr.
Pitt. She has talked of benefiting them in her
will, for the noble fight they have made against
Sir Robert Walpole.

PULTENEY. Chesterfield! There's no working with Chesterfield: and Mr. Pitt — why, the Pitts are all mad. Do you remember old Governor Pitt, and then his son Thomas, and now his son again, not to mention Miss Ann? They would all cut each others' throats, or at least each others' purse-strings. A family like her's, always bickering truculently and violently among themselves! They are just the people the old war-horse would wish to benefit.

POPE. They are the only ones she feels have rid her of her bugbear, and got nothing in return — and Lord Cobham, who needs nothing. She was terrified of Sir Robert, believing that he was ruining England from his love of power, and she bought land feverishly, selling out all her stocks, certain that soon he would pass a sponge over all money lent to the government.

PULTENEY. A miserable old age of fear and hatreds. Those of us who are wise, Mr. Pope, prepare in advance for as gracious a senility as possible, and we learn by middle-age that we must sacrifice much to preserve the little that is precious — family, friends, and a mind gay enough to be detached. She should have learnt, if not from herself, at least from others; but then, well, we know

> felix quicumque dolore
> alterius disces posse cavere tuom.

POPE. She is unable to quote the classics, as you so notoriously are, my lord; her favourite quotation, with which she whiles away the time when she is wheeled about in her chair, and is tired of listening to her mechanical organ which has but eight tunes, is from Mr. Dryden's

> When I consider life, 'tis all a cheat,
> Yet fooled with hope, men favour the deceit . . .

You know the rest.

PULTENEY. She may be tired of waiting for chymick gold, she has amassed enough of the more ordinary commodity. And, after all, what has she to complain of? She had a moment, a long moment, of power, which to her was happiness. She was the greatest woman of her time, she shone in glory, and she was married to the greatest man, whose glory is imperishable. She should not have wanted every thing, every person, to be subservient to her will for ever. Most of us would be glad to have such glories to look back to in our old age.

POPE. When you are hungry, is it of any use to remember the banquet you had last week? Many desires fade as one grows old; the gratification of youthful lusts seems foolish once the lusts have departed; many things are such that the possession of them dims their brightness; but it is rare that once a man or woman has tasted power, power loses its glamour. It is like blood to the lion-whelp; the longing only disappears with death.

PULTENEY. Perhaps it is wise never to taste power; the wisest men will hesitate to accept it when offered them. It is like Pandora's box; we rush to grasp it, and when we open it, it mocks us with the evils that fly out.

POPE. Ah! My Lady Duchess will be happy to hear the reason why one who seemed to have fought for the box so long and so strenuously should have taken his hand away from it when it was already in his grasp. What did my Lord Orford say — 'the two most insignificant fellows in England'?

PULTENEY. It is getting late, Mr. Pope; I have for too long broken in upon your avocations.

H   III

I am glad to find you in such good fettle. I will bid you good-day.

POPE. Good-day, my lord. I thank you for the honour of this visit. I am proud to know so philosophic a statesman, determined to pass the rest of his days in calm of mind — shall I add, 'all passion spent'? [*To himself, as Pulteney goes.*] Ah! So! The little wasp of Twickenham can sting yet.

THE DUKE OF NEWCASTLE

THE DUKE OF NEWCASTLE

A Conversation between Lord Chesterfield and Lieut.-General Irwine. At Blackheath. July, 1769.

CHESTERFIELD. And those, Mr. Irwine, are my cantelupe melons: but we will look at 'em another time; for even my third leg, this wooden fellow, is getting tired — indeed it has to bear most of the weight of my crazy old carcase. Half an hour is the most I can hobble at a time. If you will help me upstairs, we will sit in the gallery, look at the view, and talk.

IRWINE (*shouting*). I hope that I shall be so robust when I reach your age.

CHESTERFIELD. Eh? (*guessing*). I am beyond flattery, being no longer a statesman. But I must be the talkative one, since you would soon grow hoarse with making me hear: deafness is my hereditary right, the only one I believe in. That's well, your left shoulder: my weight won't fatigue you; we Stanhopes were always ridiculously small.

(*They sit in the gallery.*)

115

IRWINE.   Wasn't that a portrait of the Duke of Newcastle on the stairway?

CHESTERFIELD.   Taken years ago, as you could see.

IRWINE.   He must have been very old when he died, if he was at all as old as he looked.

CHESTERFIELD.   Let me see . . . he was some fourteen months older than I was . . . he must have been born in the summer of '93, and he died last November. That makes him seventy-six. I think I wrote you the news.

IRWINE.   You did indeed: you told me that he was at last dead, and for the first time quiet.

CHESTERFIELD.   I don't know what post they will find for him in heaven to make it a heaven to him: if he were not allowed to plague himself with affairs, he would think he was in hell. His ruling passion was the agitation, the bustle, and hurry of business, and to think of him as quiet is to conceive him miserable. He was always in a hurry, as though he could never be in time.

IRWINE.   I have even seen him running.

CHESTERFIELD.   He always ran — on tip-toe. Ha! I remember once telling him that by his fleetness one would think him the courier, not the author of the letters he was carrying. He was like quicksilver — only he didn't shine so bright.

IRWINE. I was astonished that he was always in so visible a state of fluster.

CHESTERFIELD. He was such a bundle of weaknesses that he could never make up his mind; and when it was made up for him, he dreaded the consequences. Everything alarmed him: he could have been still only in a frozen world. Even when I brought in my Bill for the reform of the calendar — and what could be more harmless than that? — he begged me 'not to stir matters that had long been quiet,' called my Bill, a little question of office reform, 'a bold undertaking', and added that he didn't love new-fangled things.

IRWINE. Like a man afraid to move a chair in a room for fear the whole house should tumble down! But he must sometimes have had to decide?

CHESTERFIELD. Never willingly, I believe: he didn't even choose his own wife!

IRWINE. That is not unusual, my Lord, in great families.

CHESTERFIELD. Oh, when there is family pressure; but he was his own master. What he did was to choose an intermediary to choose for him; what d'ye think of that? I had the story from old Sir John Vanbrugh, whom he employed as go-between. You wouldn't remember him, I suppose?

IRWINE. He must have died before I was born.

CHESTERFIELD. Dear, dear! so he must! Sir John was building Claremont for him, and at the same time Blenheim for the Duchess of Marlborough; and as the Duchess had a granddaughter, Sir John thought he could easily combine one business with t'other if he proposed Lady Harriet Spencer. He did so, and the Duke was taken with the idea, more than with the lady; but he shilly-shallied, as he would, put it off for a year, wondered this and that, asked too big a dowry — while the Duchess, as Sir John said, wanted a grandson-in-law, like all other things, both good and cheap: so . . .

IRWINE. She cannot have been easy to manage: I have read Mr. Pope's character of Atossa.

CHESTERFIELD. She was a friend of mine, Mr. Irwine: I will allow nobody but myself to say anything against her. The long and short of it is that after months of haggling, he was brought to it by thinking it would be pleasant to have children descended from the great Duke of Marlborough.

IRWINE. Which he never had.

CHESTERFIELD. Which, as you say, he never had. Just as well, perhaps: he would never have found time to look after them.

IRWINE. When I became a Parliament-man, I used sometimes to go to his levees, if I could spare the unconscionable time he kept us people waiting.

CHESTERFIELD. And then when he came, the illiberal, degrading familiarity of his address! How he accosted, hugged, embraced everybody, and made them fulsome promises he would not have wished to keep even if he had had the power!

IRWINE. The odd fact is that he had any power at all.

CHESTERFIELD. He loved it; he was as jealous of it as an impotent lover is of his mistress, without activity of mind enough to enjoy or exert it: yet, as I said, he dreaded power, and could not bear a share even in the appearances of it — it was Sir Robert who wished it, or Carteret who insisted, or Lord Hardwicke who pressed it urgently, whenever it couldn't be laid at the King's door. I have known him throw himself weeping on Lord Hardwicke's neck, imploring him to support him in a situation which wouldn't have irked a junior clerk for a moment. You know the story of the freedom of Bristol?

IRWINE. When it was conferred on him and Mr. Pitt? I heard no details.

CHESTERFIELD. One would have thought that a man who already had more than forty years' experience of business and Court matters would have given five minutes to composing an answer to the offer. But not so his Grace. He drew out a draft, as long as the most tedious dispatch from the most long-winded foreign minister and — sent it to Lord Hardwicke, with marginal queries, including one as to whether he should consult Mr. Pitt. Why the Lord Chancellor should concern himself doesn't appear. I don't know whether Lord Hardwicke gave much thought to the screed: he answered that he was sure his Grace could want no advice, but that in his humble opinion the draft was much too long. The Duke industriously blackened ten more large sides of paper, and finally the mountain of stationery, after great labour, gave birth to a mouse-reply of four lines. It was Stone who told me.

IRWINE. Stone, that was a mysterious figure!

The gossip went that it was Stone who was really minister, while the Duke traded the boroughs.

CHESTERFIELD. Well, no. It is true that to write to his Grace or to write to Stone was much the same thing, and that Stone knew all that was in the Duke's mind; and he would often have been at a loss without his Under-Secretary to tell him what his mind really was: but it was the Duke who led the dance. Did you know that at one time, when the Duke was not on speaking terms with his brother, who was then first minister, they used to converse through Stone, even when they were together in the same room? It was, 'Mr. Stone, would you be so kind as to tell Mr. Pelham . . .'; and 'Mr. Stone, would you be so good as to inform his Grace . . .'; and the worthy man would trot from one to the other and back again with an admirable gravity it was hard to imitate.

IRWINE. I never knew Mr. Pelham. I understand he was not at all like his brother.

CHESTERFIELD. He had great good sense, but no shining parts; and I have now come to think that in politics good sense is more valuable than brilliance. Mr. Pelham had a steady resolution, unlike his brother, and showed great candour in his behaviour. He never took refuge in cunning, that dark sanctuary of incapacity. An honourable man; a well-wishing minister! But indeed the Duke also was the last two. When he retired from business in 1762, he was above four-hundred thousand pounds poorer than when he went into it.

IRWINE. Money well spent in corruption; but at least it came from his own pocket.

CHESTERFIELD. He was disinterested, unlike Sir Robert Walpole. He twice refused a pension. He did, it is true, submit himself to that abominable system of bribery which if it is not stopped — and God knows how it is to be stopped now — will bring the country to ruin.

IRWINE. It was, I suppose, the source of his power. How else could he have been in office some forty-five years, and for some of the time first minister?

CHESTERFIELD. Without his wealth, he would, of course, have been a mere feather; but it is not wealth alone, even in these days, that can give power. It is true that he had no superior parts, no eminent talents, but he was not such a fool as the public supposed, as indeed he liked them to suppose. The whiffling activity of his body was

partly a disguise: and behind it he had indefatig-
able industry, perseverance, which gave him a
lever, added to a singular knowledge of Court
craft, and a servile compliance with the will of
the sovereign for the time being, whether George
the first, second, or third — though with his
present Majesty it did not avail him much. It
never ceases to amaze me how men of standing
and even of common sense, men of affairs, with
a knowledge of mankind and of worldly traffic,
still feel awe in the presence of kings, who are
usually far worse brought up than themselves,
and infinitely more ignorant.

IRWINE. His Majesty, after all, is the head of
the State, the keystone of the Constitution.

CHESTERFIELD. Oh, by all means; but no man
stands in awe of a keystone. No, it is more than
that. They are like boys in the presence of their
schoolmaster; if the King frowns, they feel
whipped; if he smiles, they feel entitled to a half-
holiday. I was never more struck by this than
in the great revolution of '46 — you will remember
the heaven-sent forty-eight hour ministry?

IRWINE. I was not much more than a boy at the
time, and my interests were less in politics than
in my military duties.

CHESTERFIELD. Come, General, so serious already. No tributes to Venus? For shame!

IRWINE. By my 'interests' I meant rather what I thought of in my spare time, the time I could spare from the more serious pursuits that you mention: but I nevertheless remember the occasion you refer to, when Lords Granville and Bath laughed up to London to take the Seals, and then were laughed away again after fingering them. I was in Ireland at the time.

CHESTERFIELD. Ah, to be sure; and so was I. It was then and there indeed that I first met you.

IRWINE. And when I met the best Viceroy Ireland ever had.

CHESTERFIELD. Say, the most Irish Viceroy. When I was there I panted to get away, but I have often wished that time back again. But about this ministry! The plot, if you like to call it so, was thrashed out at the beginning of '45; the case was this: the Pelhams were nominally in power, and stronger than ever before, since they had at last gathered in the remnant of the old opposition.

IRWINE. Meaning yourself.

CHESTERFIELD. Oh, and the Cobham faction, and half-patriots, half malcontent Whigs — these are old stories now. Parliament was behind them and their policy. Carteret, who at about that time became Granville, had gone from public view, but he was still in the closet; and he and Lord Bath had the key to the back door: they were virtually the Cabinet, and the King forced their policy on his ostensible ministers. The issue was, as I urged in letter after letter to the Duke — for I was then at the Hague — were the King's servants his ministers, or, really, the servants of other ministers? Again and again I implored him to resign with his colleagues in a body, and before Parliament rose: for once it was gone they were powerless. What! the Duke said, resign all together? Why, that is conspiracy: it is indeed high treason. If one or two of you resign, I answered, the King can replace you, but who in heaven or earth is to fill the posts if we all go? This is unheard of, the Duke would protest: what would his Majesty do without us? Exactly! I used to reply, show now that you're indispensable. Oh but, he havered, that wouldn't be respectful. I told him that it was not the respectfulness of measures I considered, but their expedience, their prudence, their necessity. But Parliament rose, and his Majesty went to Hanover without anything being done. And in the autumn, the rebellion in Scotland made such a step inopportune.

IRWINE. I forget what it was brought the Duke's courage up to the sticking point, if I ever knew.

CHESTERFIELD. It was over the question of admitting Mr. Pitt to office, or rather to the post of Secretary at War. The King had a mortal dislike to Mr. Pitt, and refused ever to see him. Matters might have been arranged, but that Lord Bath, with Lord Granville behind the scenes, but pretending not to be there, whispered in the King's ear as the toad did that of Eve in Milton's poem, insinuating that his ministers were affronting him. After a great to-do, the details of which I forget, the members of the ministry heroically decided to resign, and for two or three days there was a rare procession of White Staffs and Seals going up the steps of St. James's. Funds fell while the new cabal hawked places about, and could find no takers. You know the rest. The King grumbled as usual that the ministers were the king in this country, and everybody came back. The matter for amused consideration is their abhorrence of the idea of opposition — never, never, they declared, would they band themselves into so horrid a thing — and the sense of guilt they carried about with them after their action.

IRWINE. You yourself, my Lord, declared when you resigned the Seals that you would never go into opposition.

CHESTERFIELD. I had earned my rest. Were not eleven years of opposition enough for my share? I had had my fill of patriots.

IRWINE. I presume that when Dr. Johnson described patriotism as the last refuge of the scoundrel, he was referring to political faction which aims at disturbing the government?

CHESTERFIELD. All parties claim the monopoly of patriotism: those who have the places, that is the money, are exceedingly desirous to keep them; and those who have them not are as desirous to get them, that is the money. I had nothing to ask.

IRWINE. But had the Duke anything to ask?

CHESTERFIELD. Nothing — but the being in business. He itched to be at it. It may have been habit, since from the time he was made Lord Chamberlain in 1716, until 1762, except for a few months in '56–'57, he was always in office. His *otium* was always *sine dignitate*, just as his business was. He was Secretary of State for some thirty years together, from 1724 to 1754, when, his brother dying, he became first minister. And then, rather than be nothing, he allowed himself to be made Lord Privy Seal in '65. It was a disease.

IRWINE. I always wondered how, with his notorious ignorance, he could even maintain an appearance as Secretary of State.

CHESTERFIELD. Oh, I know the stories: 'Cape Breton an island? Really? Show it me on the map! So it is! I must go and tell the King. He'll be delighted:' and 'Minneapolis must be defended. Send troops to Minneapolis. Where is Minneapolis?' But he was far from ignorant of foreign affairs: he had acquired an enormous amount of information, which he stored away in the wallet of his memory.

IRWINE. Alms for oblivion?

CHESTERFIELD. By no means: but he was inclined to remember only what was agreeable. When I was Secretary of State, at the time of the Austrian Succession war, he wouldn't listen to what I told him, that the Dutch were bankrupt; but he easily accepted the absurd lies Lord

Sandwich told him to the contrary effect. I was the better informed, as events proved.

IRWINE. He must have been an uncomfortable colleague.

CHESTERFIELD. One never knew where one stood. You remember when Lord Harrington finally resigned in '46 (when I took his place) it was because his Grace corresponded behind his back with Lord Sandwich, who was in Lord Harrington's department. When Lord Harrington complained to the King, his Majesty, who had never forgiven him his part in the forty-eight hour ministry, bluntly told him he supposed he might correspond with his ministers abroad by what canal he chose. But his Grace preferred to be indirect; he was terrified he might miss something, and he behaved in exactly the same way with me. At the beginning he told Lord Sandwich that as the two Secretaries were of one mind on policy, it was enough for him to write to me. But soon it was, 'How is it I never hear from Lord Sandwich? Why does Lord Sandwich write only to you? Why does he never write to me?' I had to tell Lord Sandwich to hearten his Grace occasionally with a private letter, mixing some business in it. I would not be jealous, I said.

Little things please some people, I told him. But soon Lord Sandwich ceased to write me anything but office letters, and I was always finding the ground cut from under my feet. Finally, when Bentinck came over to discuss Dutch affairs, affairs for which I was responsible, I was the only man in the kingdom he was on no account allowed to see. I felt no pique, but it was useless for me to remain. So I quitted.

IRWINE. His views differed from yours?

CHESTERFIELD. He was incurably optimistic. He would go into the Closet and tell the King there was good news; and when he came out I would ask him what the good news was, for I could see none in what he had said. Then he would run away. He would never believe what he didn't want to think true. He thought, for instance, that if the Austrians said they would put sixty thousand men into the field, sixty thousand men would appear. Subsidies was his only notion of foreign politics — he thought he could buy states as he could buy placemen: that and Chloe.

IRWINE. Chloe?

CHESTERFIELD. How! did you never experience Chloe? — more properly M. Clouet, his French chef? You missed a good thing, one which you especially would have appreciated. When representatives came from abroad, he would instruct Chloe to stuff them well. You may sometimes induce the right frame of mind in a man if you flatter his stomach.

IRWINE.   Did Chloe ever feed Lord Chatham? There was an odd pair to go minuetting together. The Duke cannot have much enjoyed the dance, and I often wondered how you managed to bring them close enough.

CHESTERFIELD.   It was the most curious role I ever found myself in. I warned the Duke he would have trouble with his gouty wife, as I used to call Mr. Pitt — or as you rightly say, Lord Chatham, to him: but I deserved no credit for marrying 'em. It had to be; neither could hold office without the other. Indeed Mr. Pitt bullied the Duke, but the Duke enjoyed that also. After all, he managed the party, the secret service funds, the patronage, those were his delight: Mr. Pitt managed the war and the House.

IRWINE.   Which being in the other House, the Duke could not do.

CHESTERFIELD.   And could not have done as a commoner. To lead men one must be able to move men. The House of Commons is largely *peuple*; and, as the Cardinal de Retz used to say, *quiconque rassemble le peuple, l'émeut.* You will not mind my lapsing into French, seeing you are yourself so good a Frenchman, as Madame de Monconseil assures me.

IRWINE. She flatters me. The Duke was no speaker, like Mr. Pitt.

CHESTERFIELD. I confess I never altogether liked Mr. Pitt, he was too flamboyant, too theatrical for me: but he could indeed move the people. He carried with him the strength of thunder, and the splendour of lightning. The marriage worked admirably for a time, though the gouty wife would often enough remove herself in the sulks. But the Duke as a popular leader? No! Did you not think, privately, Mr. Irwine, that his face resembled that of a sheep?

IRWINE. Sometimes, certainly, it looked as crest-fallen. I was sorry for him at the end, when Lord Bute took the reins out of his hands. That was a terrible story about the archbishopric of York.

CHESTERFIELD. I do not know it: I know nothing these days. The coffee-houses are better informed than I am: they know everything.

IRWINE. I believe he recommended a Whig to the prelacy, and Lord Bute answered, 'If your Grace thinks so highly of him, I wonder that you did not promote him when you had the *power.*' This to the first minister!

CHESTERFIELD. Meekness and humility are Christian virtues: I didn't know my poor old cousin had so great a share of 'em. What a strange thing this fever of power is! My grandfather Halifax used to doubt whether business was fit for a man of sense, and, moreover, it was the under-side of power the Duke of Newcastle loved. I wonder what posterity will think of him? for history will not be able to neglect him. Historians are necessarily ignorant; and perhaps what seems to matter so much to us will seem of little weight to them, for the past, which seems to teach us so much, often teaches us wrong. But I grow prosy: deaf men converse with themselves so much, they may forget that others may be listening to their droning.

IRWINE. Your Lordship has been too kind, too patient of my ignorance.

CHESTERFIELD. Stuff! the kindness has been yours, I feel; certainly the patience. When we grow old and ready to go, with nothing before us, it is only by thinking of the past that we can manage to avoid the present.

LORD CHESTERFIELD

LORD CHESTERFIELD

A Conversation between The Hon. Horace Walpole and Dr. Matthew Maty (Principal Librarian at the British Museum). Strawberry Hill, 1776.

WALPOLE. Ah! Dr. Maty! How charming of you to jolt all this way from your ancient books to see my new-born trifles. You found your way easily?

MATY. I had come to Twitnam before, to view Mr. Pope's grotto.

WALPOLE. Toy for toy, I like my Gothic ingenuities better: I will show you my latest child; you must dote on it, or I shall not love you. But first let us sit down a little — you must be tired — here, at this window: we will watch the most charming of rivers flowing down. Look! there is Cliveden, one of the *pièces* of Twickenham-shire.

MATY. Cliveden?

WALPOLE. Where our dear Mrs. Kitty Clive, is, as you men of letters would say, passing the evening of her life. But I doubt you are too eruditely busied ever to waste an evening at the theatre?

MATY. Busied, yes, Mr. Walpole; but not now as you may suppose. Following your example, I am adding a book to the national store. Not my skill, but the subject, will, I trust, make it a worthy addition.

WALPOLE. Oh? Some abstract disquisition, I fear, far above my poor head.

MATY. My work is less remote. I am inditing a memoir of my late good friend and patron, Lord Chesterfield. I may confess it was partly on that account I proposed to myself the honour of this visit, hoping that you might have some delightful reminiscence to impart.

WALPOLE. A memoir! What writings are more delicious than memoirs? I love them to a degree, and my fingers itch to turn over the pages of yours. Memoirs should be rich and fluent, as yours no doubt will be, Dr. Maty; easy and — yes, voluble: I had almost said garrulous: well spiced with anecdote, and not always of the most creditable kind. What would Suetonius be without the scandalous gossip? Be a little of an old woman as you write it, dear Doctor! We want to see the whole man, and not some puppet dressed up for a royal drawing-room. Men do not live in full dress; and we like to see them even when they would least wish to be seen, in their dressing-gowns.

MATY. Ahem!

WALPOLE. You look dubious. We shall expect more than a sartorial exercise from you.

MATY. I am preparing the work for his Countess, not under her eye, but — feelings must be spared, Mr. Walpole: so good a lady, who revered her husband so much!

WALPOLE. That does indeed alter the case. But tell me, since her Ladyship cannot hear us, was not my Lord of a somewhat easy conscience? When as a young man he preferred to be known on his rambles as Mr. Grimes, so Mrs. Constantia Muilman, Con Phillips that was, tells us in her *Apology?*

MATY. Mrs. Muilman! That idle story was refuted by the 'Lady of Quality' who exposed her.

WALPOLE. And Lady Frances Shirley — 'Fanny blooming fair?' whom he stole from my poor friend Lovel, though indeed he had as little right to her as Lord Chesterfield had. Which of them was it that drove her to sit at Mr. White-field's feet in Lady Huntingdon's chapel?

MATY. Platonic, Mr. Walpole!

WALPOLE. Maybe; but that was poor consolation for her Ladyship. Indeed, must not such an attachment be harder than another for a wife to forgive? An idle frivolity, a mere physical escapade, that lasts but a summer's day, is more readily pardoned than an affair where the head is enthralled. That endures. And la Bouchet? Will you be silent about her in your memoir?

MATY. Her Ladyship was always well disposed towards Mademoiselle du Bouchet, and shared some of my Lord's feelings for his son. She seemed to regret his death almost as much as his father did.

WALPOLE. I used to see the son from time to time, when he was in Parliament: a gawky youth he seemed to me, who did not know how to hold his hands, and muttered and spluttered so, that one began to think he must be talking German. His one speech in the House was lamentable. And what labour Lord Chesterfield wasted on this unworthy object! One thinks of a man trying to fashion a delicate Sèvres figure out of London Clay. The graces, the Guido graces his Lordship called them, did he not? — the Titian tints — the Corinthian pillar on a Tuscan base! Is it not all a little pitiful, Dr. Maty?

MATY. I think Lord Chesterfield wished to supply his son with such gifts as might replace those he had failed to give him by his birth. A natural son must rise by natural talents.

WALPOLE. What faith in education! As though it could turn dross into gold!

MATY. Philip was honest and good-natured; he had a fund of affection, and an intelligence above the common. But he was unfitted to be a man of affairs, the only career his father would consider for him. His lordship once suggested to him in satire that he might become a University professor; but without going so far, I venture to think he would have made a tolerable don, for he liked learning, and had accumulated a good store of it.

WALPOLE. I was struck when reading the letters, to find how much they came from the heart. There was real love mingled with the sternness of the parent, which surprised me in one who seemed so much a stranger to the emotions, who made pretence to be imperturbable, and above the mere vanities of feeling.

MATY. A hundred men, Mr. Walpole, could testify to his kindness and consideration — the Bishop of Waterford, Mr. Dayrolles, poor Mr.

Hammond, whose death deprived us of so much graceful verse — not to mention myself. If ever a man was loyal in his friendships, it was he.

WALPOLE. And implacable in his hatreds. I can never quite forgive him for leading the pack which hounded my father, best of men, out of office, and sent him to his grave from disappointment.

MATY. Love of principle — I speak without prejudice, Mr. Walpole — not hatred of persons, actuated him. You will remember that he was the only one of his faction to wish Lord Orford joy when he came to take his seat in the House of Lords.

WALPOLE. He knew it to be 'the hospital for incurables!'

MATY. Come, sir, I pray you: that is unjust. Emotions he had, but jealousy or bitterness against persons he never felt, even against the Duke of Newcastle, who betrayed him, or Lord Sandwich, his partner in the betrayal.

WALPOLE. Oh, Jemmy Twitcher! he is below hatred.

MATY. Indeed, in all his political life there is no trace of rancour. As well accuse him of that as of self-seeking.

WALPOLE. Of self-seeking I acquit him entirely, though I once thought differently.

MATY. He was the soul of honour and justice.

WALPOLE. When in office, yes, perhaps: I have no means of knowing. But when in opposition, he was not just. You remember the great lantern that hangs in the hall of Chesterfield House?

MATY. A noble ornament.

WALPOLE. But when it hung at Houghton, it proved my father's rapacity; it flaunted his ill-gotten wealth, so the Patriots, with Lord Chesterfield among 'em, declared: it was a brand of infamy. In some strange way it recovered its innocency on the road from Norfolk to Mayfair!

MATY. That was a long time ago.

WALPOLE. You reprove me justly: and if I once harboured resentment against Lord Chesterfield, in his later years he won me over, with his candour, his generosity, and, yes, his wisdom. He carried his wit to the very door of his coffin, and that is a sign of courage.

MATY. His good-breeding deserted him only with his life, as Dr. Warren, who attended him, bore witness. He uttered his last words when Mr. Dayrolles came to see him. 'Give Dayrolles a chair,' he murmured.

K   143

WALPOLE. Indeed? Admirable! But what else could he have said? We might all with our last breath compass an invitation to an old friend to sit down. But I saw something of him in his later years.

MATY. You visited him?

WALPOLE. Rarely. I was afraid of the dog.

MATY. Poor Loyola! He had an evil reputation.

WALPOLE. And his master and mistress always sided with him. I remember Mrs. Jepson telling me, who sat in the drawing-room in fear and trembling, that she asked Lady Chesterfield how to avoid offending Loyola; and was told 'dat she tought de best way vas not to look dat corner of de room.' No, I was thinking of the time he visited me here.

MATY. He visited you here?

WALPOLE. He did me that honour. He came to see my books, which had pricked his curiosity, though he always cared more for what an author had to say than for the way in which you dressed him. But when his eyes became weak, he grew to like good printing.

MATY. His deafness, depriving him of what he most loved, conversation, drove him ever more to books for companionship, to the injury of his eyes . . .

WALPOLE. He couldn't talk to his pineapples and cantelupes all day long, eh, Dr. Maty?

MATY. . . . but he never cared for old books, and used to banter me for my love of them.

WALPOLE. He told his son, I think, that the best editions were the newest, unless the editors were fools. Perhaps he carried his hatred of pedantry too far; but this I will say, he despised all kinds of cant.

MATY. Tell me of his visit.

WALPOLE. It was only a year or two before his death. He hobbled on sticks, his body looked even smaller than it used to do, his head bigger; and he could hardly hear. But his manner was so exquisite, that I forgot his infirmities. I thought him handsome in his old age, with his sharp beak of a nose, his heavy eyebrows, and that chin, which seemed to jut out more than ever, owing to his lips being sunken. Didn't someone once say that he was like a stunted giant? To me, he was like some terrific dwarf.

MATY. He always complained of the 'ridiculous Stanhope size', and was glad that his heir would soon outdo it. And then?

WALPOLE. I had made him a few verses in his honour, printed at my press here, as a little gesture of esteem.

MATY. May I see them? Would you give me that pleasure?

WALPOLE. I will find them; ah! here they are. I will read them to you, so that my voice can supply the defects of my metre. You will remember that he was a great friend of Mr. Pope's.

MATY. 'How shall I Pult'ney, Chesterfield forget,
While Roman virtues charm, and Attic wit?'

WALPOLE. I was not much struck by Lord Bath's Roman virtues. However, here are my verses: I don't pretend they are the most elegant ever written.

MATY. I am never a critic of what is not pretentious.

WALPOLE. Few paces hence, beneath yon grottoed road,
From dying Pope the last sweet accents flowed.
O Twitnam! would the friend of Pope but bless
With some immortal strain thy favour'd press,
The happier emblem would with truth depose,
That where one Phœnix died, another rose.

MATY. Very well indeed: you have spaced the

cæsuras admirably. And what did his Lordship think of them?

WALPOLE. The old man was pleased at the compliment — though I do not know whether he remarked the cæsuras! He said, his eyes twinkling, that I must have known the invitation was a safe one, as he was unlikely to burst into an immortal strain — to posterity's loss: and that though he might be reserved for ultimate burning, he would prefer a more normal death in his bed to roasting like the Phœnix.

MATY. He was, beyond doubt, the wittiest man of his time. Do you recall any of his strokes, Mr. Walpole?

WALPOLE. I had a great number repeated to me; but I think best of all I like his action when *la généalogeomanie*, as I may call it, was at its height. He put up two very mediocre heads in his library, and called them Adam de Stanhope and Eve de Stanhope; excellent ridicule!

MATY. He had less pride of birth than any man I have met. He always regarded it as mere luck that he had not been born a groomporter.

WALPOLE. But tell me, Dr. Maty, you who

147

knew him so well, how was it that he never had more weight in politics? Surely, with his gifts and his knowledge he should have been able to make his opinions tell? But Lord Hardwicke used to say that at the Council-table he never proffered a suggestion of his own, nor opposed another man's. Did he expect miracles to happen, and that his view would waft itself into other heads by some kind of infection? Why was he content to become, as he said himself, the third *commis*, in the kingdom?

MATY. The Bishop of Waterford has written to me that Lord Chesterfield told him, on resigning, that he was quitting because he found that in politics so many things had to be done that it was not right to do.

WALPOLE. Forgive me if I am a trifle sceptical on that point, Dr. Maty. Such sentiments would, no doubt, please the good Bishop; but Lord Chesterfield must have known what business meant before he accepted office.

MATY. He may at the moment have felt what he told the Bishop; but perhaps the truth was, as he wrote to Mr. Dayrolles, that he had been behind the scenes of both pleasure and business, had seen all the dirty pulleys and poor tallow lights that serve to dazzle the spectators — I forget his exact words — and that he was glad to retire from the glorious sham.

WALPOLE. Perhaps it was that, always liking things to be precise, he could not suffer the continual flutter and frippery of politics, where everybody does everything, and nothing happens. The Duke of Newcastle must have been maddening to work with — with his hubble-bubble manner — his effusion, his kisses, his tears, and his inability ever to make up his mind. Lord Chesterfield's ideas were so clear-cut, that not being able to make people, and indeed things, conform to them, must have irked him intolerably. Perhaps he lived too much by theory; what do you think, Dr. Maty?

MATY. He was practical enough in Ireland, where he was not only loved, but effective. He kept the Irish quiet during the rebellion of '45, when they might well have caused trouble; and he even checked the excesses in claret of the Castle company, which was perhaps a more difficult piece of work. In spite of a strict administration — he abolished jobbery — he proved most popular; and the crowd followed him down to the pier to bid him farewell, and wish for his quick return. He went on foot, and took no precautions against assault.

WALPOLE. His pose of humility when there filled me with amusement at the time; but it had its effect.

MATY. He was really humble, Mr. Walpole.

WALPOLE. And *volto scuolto e pensieri stretti?* I venture to think that he had intellectual pride, at least. He could not suffer fools gladly. Perhaps that was why he could rule well when he could rule alone, as in Ireland, but was restive and mum when in Council in England.

MATY. Who would have thought that a man with so much scepticism — he was at best a Deist — could act so boldly in Ireland, for all action is an act of faith.

WALPOLE. Faith? You surprise me, dear Doctor. It was certainly odd how a man who so despised the mob could have had so much faith in its common sense.

MATY. But he never despised individuals; it was, perhaps, on individual common sense that he relied.

WALPOLE. A perilous foundation! Hardened punter that he was — you will remember that he gambled even with the crooked-fingered German

Baron at Bath, whom we knew would cheat him at picquet — he must have realized that common sense is helpless before the passions.

MATY. Not altogether. He studiously refrained from gambling while in office.

WALPOLE. That is true, no man, when he wished, had more self-control. Perhaps that is why he could never sway men. He could rule them, but that is another thing. Both he and his notions seemed too much cut to patterns, admirable patterns, but he could not drive the nail that would go. He thought he could make men act by keeping their minds amused, when he should have tried to arouse their prejudices. Oh, he knew what was needed, he told his son this very thing, but he could not bring his fastidious self to act the actor. That is why, I think, his speeches were so utterly without effect. His virtuosity was extraordinary; one might model one's self on his form: and I think the best speech I ever heard was on a motion to reject the address. His attacks on the Stage Licensing Bill, and on the Gin Act, were full of wit and reason — pungent wit too: but, maybe because they seemed so studied, he carried no one along with him.

MATY. Yet his enemies dreaded his wit, and his friends applauded it, as I have been told.

WALPOLE. Yes, as art — but that is not politics, my dear Doctor.

MATY. He had in himself a persuasive manner, and I think that his greatest triumph may have been the overcoming of the prejudice his Majesty King George II had against him.

WALPOLE. 'The best way to prevent the Pretender from becoming King of England would be to make him Elector of Hanover, for it is certain that the English will never fetch another King from thence.' Do you remember that, Dr. Maty? It needed some forgiving, added to all his jibes at Hanover; besides his marrying the King's natural half-sister, and suing him for some money due to her by her father's will, the will his Majesty destroyed on acceding! His wit in the papers he wrote in the *Craftsman* and other places, was scathing: the account of the waxwork soldiers is as wicked a piece of satire as I know.

MATY. His essays were admirable, full of sense and good feeling.

WALPOLE. I thought the later ones a trifle sententious; this continual girding at fashions and fopperies becomes too schoolma'amish for my taste: why waste one's wit on puppets? But the irony of his earlier ones was delightful: that phrase about 'all men who have no pensions and are out of office, think alike,' where does that come? — never mind, it was on the laudable unity of feeling in the country. But even his irony—forgive my speaking thus—was inhuman: it had no anger in it.

MATY. I do not think his Lordship ever felt anger; certainly he had no bitterness in him, no vindictiveness. Righteous indignation he would think too near enthusiasm, romanticism: things were as they had to be, and he confined himself to doing good to those people whom he knew.

WALPOLE. His sentiments were not profound.

MATY. Pardon me, Mr. Walpole: his affection for his son, as you yourself have noticed, was very deep: he never complained of him even under the keenest disappointment. Lord Scarborough he loved, and he could never think of his end without pain; for he felt that he might have saved him from raising his hand against himself had he been with him at the last.

WALPOLE. Well, well, you knew him better than I did, Dr. Maty. I only saw what the world saw, the fine figure, the dazzling wit, the man who was a little too honest to be true to life. We do not like such rectitude; and though I did not join with those who decried him, both when his will was published, and when the letters to his son appeared, yet I was glad to think that a little mud had been flung at the idol, because I liked it the better a trifle battered.

MATY. He was a great man, Mr. Walpole.

WALPOLE. Great? Ah yes, yes. Come, are you rested, Dr. Maty? I must show you my poor treasures. What d'you think of my touchstone Vespasian over by the mantelpiece? I bought it in Florence a hundred years ago. And in this cabinet. . . .